The Canary That Didn't Sing
and Other Stories

The Canary That Didn't Sing
and Other Stories

Selected and Edited by Alf McCreary

Appletree Press

First published in 2007 by
Appletree Press Ltd
The Old Potato Station
14 Howard Street South
Belfast BT7 1AP

Tel: +44 (028) 90 24 30 74
Fax: +44 (028) 90 24 67 56
Email: reception@appletree.ie
Web: www.appletree.ie

A catalogue record for this book is available from the British Library.

The Canary That Didn't Sing and Other Stories

ISBN-13: 978 1 84758 026 9

Stories selected and edited by Alf McCreary
Copy-editor: Jean Brown
Cover Design: Stuart Wilkinson
Designer: Stuart Wilkinson
Production Manager: Paul McAvoy

9 8 7 6 5 4 3 2 1

AP3427

CONTENTS

ABOUT THE EDITOR

ALF McCREARY is a well-known Belfast journalist and author, who has written over 30 books on a wide range of subjects, and countless articles for newspapers and magazines at home and abroad. He is currently the Religion Correspondent of the *Belfast Telegraph* and has won several National and Regional press awards for his work. He is a part-time tutor in writing and publishing with the Institute of Lifelong Learning at Queen's University, Belfast and also at the Irish Writers' Centre in Dublin. He was appointed MBE in the 2004 New Year's Honours List.

His books include the acclaimed biographies of the late Senator Gordon Wilson, published by Harper Collins, and Archbishop Robin Eames, published by Hodder and Stoughton. This is his fourth title for the Appletree Press. His other titles with the Belfast publisher include *Northern Ireland – A Journey with Alf McCreary*, *In St Patrick's Footsteps* and *St Patrick's Breastplate*.

INTRODUCTION

It is always a delight to introduce new writing, and the pleasure is increased when the writers are those whose work is being published for the first time. The idea for this book arose from a series of residential Writers' Weekends which have taken place for the last few years in the welcoming family ambience of Arnold's Hotel, Dunfanaghy, situated in a most beautiful part of Donegal. The hotel's Glenveagh Room, with its bookish atmosphere, its roaring fire in winter and the view of the beautiful sweep of the Donegal coastline, provided an excellent atmosphere for group discussion and sharing, while the residential dimension experienced at meal-times (and not least in the bar later on) cemented friendships that were forged in the intimacy – and exposure – of the writing process.

Each weekend's course was originally conceived as an aid to people who wanted advice about having their work published. In practice this also developed into a series of seminars on creative writing, with each participant being asked to produce new material at short notice. It was a strenuous assignment, both for the writers and also for the tutor, but it was also extremely rewarding as each individual gradually developed his or her gift. Some writers have a natural flair, while others can be helped greatly through professional advice from someone who has a long experience of the delights, challenges and pitfalls of the writing business.

It is important to underline that writing and publishing are indeed a business which is based not only on creativity, but also on hard economic realities. While subsidies, scholarships and prizes for writers do exist, they are limited, and publishers need to break even – and usually much more than that – in presenting the work of writers, especially those who have not been in print before.

The contents of this book represent a wide spectrum of writing by people from very different backgrounds and with different talents. Some had a natural talent which needed to be encouraged, while others with no pretensions to becoming a published writer, were surprised by what they could achieve through hard work, and also by stretching their talent and imagination. The end-result has been most encouraging and gratifying, and immensely creative. For my part it has been a privilege to have met and worked with such people, and I am delighted that a cross-section of their work is now published in this way. This is very special book, for all concerned.

I would like to thank those who helped along the way – including the Arnold family; Tommy Thompson who assisted with the funding; Appletree Press the publishers; and particularly Jean Brown who helped with the detailed editing and who provided such sound publishing advice. Most of all, I would like to thank the writers who trusted me, and each other, on our journey of discovery.

Alf McCreary

ARTHUR MITCHELL

The Canary That Didn't Sing

My mother kept a canary, she talked to it a lot, and it rewarded her by singing sweetly back to her. She called it Joey and looked after it with great care and attention, as if it was one of her own children. This was no surprise really for I, her youngest child and the last one at home, had left three years before to study medicine at University and she had no children around her to shower with affection. When visitors were in the house Joey would sing enthusiastically as well as sweetly. He must have felt that they challenged his relationship with my mother, because as soon as the conversation started, so would Joey. The louder they talked the louder and louder he sang. It could become quite difficult to follow the conversation with his persistent singing in the background. Mother, of course, had a cure. She would go to the drawer in the sideboard, take out a large tray cloth and gracefully throw it over the cage. The result was instant silence! It seemed that if Joey couldn't see the origin of the conversation, he obviously didn't feel challenged by it, and in return he didn't sing.

Canaries, like any other living creature, have a certain life expectancy and in Joey's case it was obviously running out. He began to sing less and to take less care of his plumage, and his activity began to slow noticeably. My mother was proud of her youngest son who was half way through his medical degree at University, so when I came home one weekend she put me on the spot about Joey. I had to listen to an extensive history of his condition, and I was asked to make a diagnosis and then formulate an appropriate line of treatment, which, hopefully, would subsequently lead to Joey's rejuvenation. I was struggling, because my knowledge of avian anatomy was almost non-existent. Indeed, that was not my only deficiency because my knowledge of avian physiology, diseases and, in particular their treatment, was also non-existent. I had a real credibility problem with my mother! However, I did what all good physicians learn to do early in their careers – I told her that it was not just a simple problem and that I would have to give it some thought. As soon as I could sort out the complexities, I would be in touch. Happily, I had bought myself some time to defend my credibility.

Back at university this unique case, code named "Operation Joey", was discussed in depth with my future wife, also a medical student. We both decided that we needed knowledge fast, so I was dispatched to a well-known pet shop in the Smithfield Market area of Belfast. There, to my relief, I found cages of healthy, vigorous singing canaries, and a helpful proprietor. I was quizzed about Joey's diet, exercise, plumage and even his celibacy, but nothing appeared relevant to this particular case. A tonic was prescribed which was to be added to Joey's drinking water. I purchased the potion, pleasantly surprised that it was not particularly expensive. It was taken home at the first opportunity, and my mother wrote down the instructions and administered it religiously.

She started with hopeful expectancy, but as the weeks passed and nothing happened, she began to despair. Joey showed no sign of improvement; indeed he became more feeble and decrepit. In desperation I returned to the pet shop in Smithfield for another clandestine consultation. I felt awful; it was just as if I was secretly trying to find out the prognosis of a dear but terminally ill relative. In the end the news was bad, no hope was given, poor Joey's problem was that "his end was nigh".

My future wife and I discussed the problem at great length, and decided that the case needed an approach of brutal realism, allied to a large dose of subterfuge. We decided that our next visit to home would have to be organised with military precision.

On the Friday, before our weekend trip, I assembled my weaponry. Cotton wool, a small bottle of ether, a cardboard box with ventilation holes and some old copies of the Belfast Telegraph in the bottom, a roll of 'Sellotape', some canary seed, a small box that once had contained a mouth organ with a satin lining, and a box of carpet tacks. On the Saturday morning I went back to the pet shop in Smithfield and bought a young and vigorous canary, a double for Joey. The new canary was placed in the cardboard box, and we set off for home, collecting my fiancée on the way. The journey was grim for both of us, for we knew what was ahead and obviously it was not easy for Joey "The Second" for he treated the old copies of the *Belfast Telegraph* with audacious and excremental disrespect on the way.

All the equipment and Joey "The Second" stayed in the car when we arrived home, to be greeted by my excited and adoring parents. They were excited, not just because we had come home for the weekend, but also because it was my mother's birthday and we were to have a special tea. First however, my future wife was to take her down to the best household furnishing shop in the town to choose something for her birthday. My father was easily persuaded to accompany them. I had unfortunately developed a convenient migraine, but I assured everybody that it would settle if I took a couple of tablets and had a "lie down" on the couch. Alone in the house, my migraine immediately disappeared and my usually well-controlled "Dr Crippen" qualities took over seamlessly. The canaries were switched, Joey "The Second" was put into the cage, the original Joey was placed in the cardboard box accompanied by a wad of cotton wool soaked in ether and the ventilation holes were sealed with 'Sellotape'. I then put a couple of carpet tacks in the drinking-water container in the cage, while I waited. It was all over in five minutes, I checked the original Joey for any signs of life and satisfied that he was indeed dead, I placed him in the satin-lined box and reverently buried him in the rose bed in the garden. I then gathered all the felonious evidence together, took it out to our car and hid it carefully beneath a travelling rug.

Returning to the house I found that Joey "The Second" had settled in well and was enjoying some seeds and water. I turned on the television and lay down on the couch. Joey "The Second" began to sing so loudly that I couldn't hear the television, and I had to get up and put a tray cloth over his cage. Thankfully, this had exactly the same effect as it had on his predecessor and instant silence resulted. After about an hour the others returned, and were delighted to find that I had recovered and that the headache had gone. I explained that I hadn't needed to take any tablets, instead I had put on the television for company, and had lain down on the couch to rest. However, Joey had begun to sing and I had to put the tray cloth over him. Both of us had then had a good rest, and my headache had gone. Mother was pleased, for she hadn't heard Joey sing for many weeks. She supposed it was because there were extra and less familiar people in the house. I encouraged her to leave the cage covered for the rest of the evening, in case the singing brought back my migraine.

We had a lovely birthday tea during which I explained to my mother that when she took the tray cloth off Joey's cage in the morning she shouldn't be surprised to find a couple of carpet tacks in his drinking water container. I admitted that I had taken professional advice from the pet shop proprietor in Smithfield, and he had informed me that the symptoms that I was describing were of avian iron deficiency. Accordingly he had advised me on the treatment. Ceremoniously I handed over the box of carpet tacks to my mother instructing her to change the drinking water twice weekly, and to put fresh tacks into it. This regime was to be carried out for six weeks, and that until the canary was fully recovered, he should be discouraged from singing too much. This could be achieved by covering his cage for several hours in the late morning, and in the late afternoon. This regime was immediately instigated, and poor Joey "The Second" was virtually prevented from singing for the rest of our stay that weekend.

Two months passed before we were home again, and during our visit mother was reminiscing about her birthday tea, and how much she had enjoyed our company on that special occasion. She again thanked us for her "official" birthday present and then added that Joey's miraculous recovery was the best birthday present she'd ever had. She considered that the diagnosis and the treatment had been absolutely correct, for he'd never looked back; indeed he looked younger every day.

Joey "The Second" lived for many more years and followed his predecessor's tradition by being a tremendous singer. I admired his beautiful colour and vigour, but most of all I admired his tolerance. After all, he had to drink metallic flavoured water for the first six weeks in his new home. He also learnt very quickly not to look unwell, become untidy or loose his vigour because if he did, for some unknown reason that he could never understand, this resulted in his mistress putting carpet tacks in his drinking water twice a week and covering his cage with a tray cloth more frequently for the next six weeks.

My mother was a bright, gifted, intelligent woman of sixty-two at that time and I always wondered if she realised that we had switched the two Joeys. I suspected that she did, but her affection for her youngest son and her appreciation for our solving such a delicate and heart-breaking problem in her life, meant she never embarrassed me by asking about it. She predeceased Joey "The Second" after a hard struggle with cancer several years later, and he lived out his days in the affectionate care of my sister. I was so thankful that we had managed to hit the right note with my mother, without me having "to sing like a canary"!

The "Second-hand" Watch

I suppose in the eyes of the law all of us were occasional criminals. Everyone indulged in a little smuggling while rationing was in force both during and after the Second World War. We all justified it, by saying that we were only augmenting the meagre diet enforced on us by rationing. However, it was the temptation of those little extras and the luxuries that drew us all into the "game". Yet the Customs and Excise still viewed it as a serious business. Not only could they confiscate the contraband, but also the vehicle, and there were stiff fines as well. However, it was the threat of being caught which added that extra excitement.

I was "the baby" of the family, five years younger than my sister, yet I remember very clearly when she passed her "Senior Certificate" examination. She had then applied successfully to become a nurse at the Royal Infirmary in Edinburgh. It was essential that my sister had a second-hand watch for her training. Time was passing quickly, and there was an air of desperation in the search, because we only had just over a week to go before her departure. Then one day Father came home from work and excitedly told Mother that he had been told that there was a good jeweller in Moville, on the Donegal shore of Lough Foyle. An expedition was hurriedly planned for the next Saturday. We would drive to Magilligan Point and take the foot passenger ferry across Lough Foyle to Moville.

The big day arrived and we were all ushered into the car. Into the boot went several full screw-topped water carriers, empty hot water bottles, a small methylated spirit stove, several torches, a kettle inside a large biscuit tin, and the makings of a good picnic tea. There were plenty of rugs, Mother had her knitting as usual, and we had our warm coats. When we arrived at Magilligan Point, the boat was already waiting for us. Mother, who was not a good sailor, chose to stay on the shore. She wrapped herself in a rug in the front seat of the car and made herself comfortable for the long wait. She bade us a fond farewell, picked up her knitting and the familiar 'clickity-clack' began, for she didn't want to watch us departing.

The wind was quite strong now and the "white horses" were rolling into the bay and breaking onto the shore. Although the boat was beached, it was still twenty feet from the water's edge, so the boatmen, who were wearing long waders, carried us out to it and bundled us aboard. It was an open boat with a small engine, and there were a dozen people on board, including the two boatmen. It sat low in the water, and as we motored out from the beach the waves crashed over the bow and the spray flew around us. The vessel heaved over the waves, wallowed in the troughs, and it was wet and cold. Some of the passengers became very sick and were hanging over the side but Father, and my brother and I, were fine. Once we got used to the violent movement of the boat, the journey became exhilarating, and even enjoyable! The time passed quickly, and soon we were tying up at the small concrete pier in Moville.

Once ashore, Father gave us a list of groceries to purchase, and said that he would meet us back at the pier in about three quarters of an hour. Meanwhile, he went off to find the jeweller's shop. Moville in those days was just a small cluster of houses and shops around the harbour, so it was not difficult to find the grocer's shop and soon we were buying sugar, sausages, cooked ham and some of the much-loved iced caramels. Clutching our purchases, we strolled back to the pier, but there was no sign of Father.

We waited around anxiously, noting that there were already some of the passengers aboard the boat. The rest arrived and began to clamber aboard, but still there was no sign of Father. We looked at each other anxiously, and just when we were about to give up and climb aboard the boat, our father appeared, strolling nonchalantly down to the pier. Then we all climbed aboard together. "Did you get the second-hand watch?" I asked quietly as we took our seats. "Shush!" hissed my brother giving me a fierce look and then glancing anxiously around. My father leant over towards me and whispered, "We'll talk about that on the way home in the car."

The wind had died away, and the sea was much calmer when we set out for the home shore. The journey was pleasant, and nobody was seasick, but it was getting cold. Father turned up the collars on our coats, and we huddled together on the wooden seat to keep warm. The boat chugged along and soon we were in the shelter of Magilligan Point in Northern Ireland. At the back of the beach we could see our car, parked where we had left it, but now sitting beside it was a large grey lorry. There was a sudden buzz of conversation in the boat. "It's the Excise!" someone exclaimed loudly. "What is the Excise?" I asked with wide-eyed innocence. "They're the Customs Officers from the border," replied Father. "The ones who used to search the car, when we were coming back from the 'South'."

"Oh, they're usually very nice," I responded, "but what are they doing here?

"They'll search us to see if we have any contraband that we shouldn't be bringing into the 'North'," replied Father. "What for instance?" I asked nervously, looking down at our carrier bags and parcels. "Oh, if you stuck to the shopping list I gave you, we'll be well within the regulations," Father replied. "What about the second-hand watch?" I whispered nervously. "Shush!" hissed my brother fiercely. Until now the Customs and the Border had been a game to me. Now with the potential arrest of my father for smuggling a watch, and the rest of us stranded in our car on the beach because my mother could not drive, meant that my stomach filled with fluttering butterflies.

Just then, the boat ran up the beach and the Customs men in their dark blue great coats walked down towards us. We were carried ashore and stood huddled in a group until we were ushered up to the side of the lorry; there a set of steps, with handrails, led up to a door. Father raised his hat to the nearest customs officer, and began to chat about the weather and the boat journey. Then he asked innocently if the customs checked all the boat arrivals, or just at random. The customs officer smiled and replied that it was usually at random, and that we were the lucky ones. Everybody laughed nervously, but I didn't think it was very funny. One by one our fellow passengers were ushered up the steps and disappeared, out of sight through the door.

Father held us back, politely allowing everyone else to go before us. Then inevitably it was our turn and Father waved us up the steps and followed behind. The lorry was brightly lit inside, there were several cubicles along one side with curtains pulled across the front, and it was obvious that people were being searched, because I could hear the conversation and see several pairs of feet moving about under the lower edge of the curtain. On a table near the back door of the lorry there was a pile of all sorts of goods. There were bags of sugar, wrapped butter, half-opened parcels of sausages, bacon and cooked ham, bolts of cloth for clothing and curtains, some pieces of jewellery and several watches. "That must be the contraband table", I thought sadly, seeing the glum faces of some of our fellow passengers, who were giving personal details to a customs officer filling out forms.

"Next!" A surly looking customs officer called out in a gruff voice and Father raised his hat politely and pushed us forward. Our carrier bags and parcels were thoroughly checked, and found to be satisfactory. Then we were taken into a cubicle one by one and searched. When I came out of the cubicle, Father was still chatting to one of the Customs Officers and he handed our carrier bags and parcels to us. "You go out to your mother in the car," he said gently. "I'll be out in a minute or two."

We left by the door in the back of the lorry, climbed down the steps, hurried over to the car and got into the back, closing the door behind us to keep out the cold evening air. "Where's your father?" asked Mother, looking up from her knitting. "He's still with the Customs," my brother replied. We sat in silence for several minutes, and I noticed that the car's windows had 'steamed up'. I wound mine down to see out.

"Did he get the watch?" Mother asked quietly. "I don't know, he wouldn't tell us and I wasn't allowed to talk about it," I replied glaring at my brother. "Well you shouldn't have asked about it when there were people around" he retorted. "Then he must have got it" Mother said knowingly as she returned to her knitting.

Five minutes later I was beginning to panic, because there was no sign of Father. I was bursting to know what was going on, but I seemed to be the only one who was interested. My brother was quiet and Mother just kept on knitting in the gathering gloom of the approaching dusk. "What if they find the watch and arrest Father?" I asked tentatively. "Oh your father would sort it all out," said Mother. "I don't think that they'd arrest him anyway. He'll be all right." But I wasn't so sure. Just then the door in the back of the lorry opened, and I could see Father silhouetted against the light inside. He was still smiling, chatting away and he raised his hat as he said goodbye, thanking everyone for their help and advice.

"Now you get that checked as soon as possible," I heard the customs officer tell him. "You never know with phlebitis and that's a definite clot, if it moves, it could be very serious."

"Thank you, I'll get it checked first thing on Monday," replied Father as he came down the steps and got into the car. He kissed my mother on the cheek, and then taking a chamois leather out of the glove compartment, he assiduously began to clean all the windows in the front of the car. He appeared to be in no hurry to leave, and when he had finished he handed the chamois to me and after I had closed my window, I cleaned all the windows in the back. "Now, I think we'll drive a little way along the road and then we'll stop, boil the kettle, make a cup of tea and fill the hot water bottles for the journey home," said Father. Irritatingly, he could be a very organised man.

When we were moving off, I couldn't contain myself any longer. "Father, did you get the second-hand watch," I asked loudly. This time it was my father who looked at me with a quizzical expression on his face. "Why do you keep asking me that? No, I didn't get a second-hand watch, I got a new watch with a second hand on it, so that your sister can count her patients' pulses when she goes off to train to be a nurse."

"Oh!" I exclaimed as the penny finally dropped, "but where did you hide it?" I asked eagerly. Father smiled, glanced at Mother, who was looking questioningly at him, chuckled and then spoke in a quiet gentle way. "Well, you know that I suffer from varicose veins and I have to wear elastic stockings for them. After I'd bought the watch I asked the jeweller in Moville if I could use his toilet and while there I slipped the watch down inside my elastic stocking."

"But didn't the customs man feel it when he searched you?" I asked. "He felt up and down my legs, to see if I had something hidden there, when he searched me."

"Oh yes, he certainly did and when he touched it, I winced and complained that it had become very hard and painful over the last few days," replied Father. "The Customs Officer was very concerned, because an uncle of his had died when a clot in his leg had moved to his lungs. He said he was suspicious that a clot had formed in the vein in my leg, because it was so hard and that I must take it easy and get it checked by a Doctor as soon as possible. I gave him my word that I would get the lump checked at the earliest opportunity, and that's what I'll do when we stop to make tea and fill the hot water bottles for the journey home."

Later we all checked the 'lump' carefully and indeed, to our relief and delight, it was not a clot but rather, a shiny new watch with a second hand, ticking away quite happily in the palm of my father's hand. My sister would be so pleased, but not half as much as we were. It was time to savour the pleasure of a successful smuggling escapade, and all our fears were quickly overcome as the 'second-hand watch' quietly ticked away.

Mr Cool and the Little Green Apples

At the end of the Second World War, I was seven years old and had just been introduced to bananas, which I loved but didn't yet know how to peel. There were 'Jersey Tom' tomatoes, too, which all of us ate. They jingled my gums, but I loved them, as well as a regular supply of sweets, iced baps and of course 'brown' lemonade. There were also luscious red and green apples, from America, but their sumptuous looks belied a rather disappointing, bland taste. My priorities were simple in those days. Summers seemed to be long and hot, with languid fishing or boating on the river, interspersed with sea and sand on the nearest beach at Portstewart.

There was also a good gang in the avenue, with a half dozen members. It was a good gang from my point of view, for several reasons. Firstly, they didn't indulge in vandalism; secondly, they were, in modern parlance, 'cross-community'. Most importantly, although they considered me too young to be a gang member, since my elder brother was one of them, they tolerated me and looked after me. I was like Dopey in *Snow White and the Seven Dwarfs* – easily distracted, and always at the rear trying to keep up.

At the end of the long summer holidays boredom had invariably set in. We were restless, on the lookout for some new challenge, something different or even daring, something that would make that summer exceptional and memorable.

What we actually discovered was just across a cornfield, and through a small gap in a beech hedge at the other side. There they hung, like clusters of emeralds, twinkling in the bright summer sun. They were apples on a tree in the middle of an orchard; but this wasn't just any old orchard. It was the orchard of a very senior policeman – the District Inspector of the Royal Ulster Constabulary, no less. My father knew him through his work in the bank, and my mother also knew his wife through the Women's Institute. A raid on such an orchard was going to be a difficult operation, and certainly disastrous if it went wrong. To be successful, it needed to be meticulously planned, and we needed good intelligence. Each gang member was given specific information to find out about the orchard's perimeter and the movements of the people who would oversee it and could cause us problems. In other words, 'we cased the joint' for several weeks.

Meanwhile, the apples grew larger and twinkled ever more temptingly in the late summer sun.

In gang headquarters, which was a neighbour's garden shed, the information was recorded and collated, and a plan was hatched. It transpired that the D.I. was on late duty every Wednesday evening, and didn't come home until after ten. His wife went to the WI once a month, also on a Wednesday. On that particular night she left the children off with her parents and didn't get home until after ten. So the house would be empty and the 'job' could be done, but we all knew that it would be a high risk. Each gang member was given a role, keeping watch on the back of the house, carrying apples and making sure that the escape route was clear. My very important task, since I was the smallest and thus the lightest, was to get myself shoved up the tree to the lowest branches, and then climb up and throw down the apples.

The appointed evening arrived, and the probing expeditionary force went out and returned. They reported that the D.I.'s wife and children had left in the car, and there was no sign of life in the house. We left operational headquarters, walked down the avenue to the field gate, and climbed over it. The corn proved to be higher than anticipated, so we walked round the side of the field rather than leave obvious tell-tale tracks through it. We reached the cover of the beech hedge, and tentatively approached the gap near the corner of the orchard.

An old rusty iron gate had been pushed into the gap and tied to the hedge on either side. The strings were soon undone and we pushed the gate over into the orchard. The final assault team crept inside. We stood nervously against the inside of the hedge, afraid to move forward, and away from the security it offered. All seemed still and quiet; there was no sign of life in the house. The curtains were open, but no lights shone out. One by one, we dashed across to the nearest tree trunk and then worked our way across the orchard from tree to tree until we were standing at the target.

When we looked up, the green apples weren't half as large as we thought they were going to be. I was grabbed roughly and heaved upward by my companions so that I could grasp the lower branches and pull myself up onto them. From there, I climbed up into the tree and was soon almost out of sight of my comrades down below. I began to pull the apples off, and carefully dropped them down to the waiting catchers. They handed them on to the carriers who stuffed them into their pockets. At first, the instructions were given in hoarse whispers, then as confidence grew, they became louder, interspersed by chuckles and eventually gleeful shouts.

Suddenly, however, there was a crash as the French windows of the study at the back of the house were thrown open. An angry, red-faced, burly man in a grey roll neck sweater, slacks and check bedroom slippers burst forth, shouting and swearing loudly. The assault ground-support team made a very unstrategic, undignified and untimely retreat. In fact, they ran like hell, leaving a trail of little green apples behind them. They jumped through the gap in the beech hedge, hurtled straight across the field through the ripening corn, and hurdled the field gate as if it wasn't there.

The D.I. puffed up to the gap in the hedge just in time to see the culprits disappear beyond the gate, and into the gathering dusk. I could see glimpses of this through the dense camouflage of thick foliage and little green apples. It all seemed to be taking place in slow motion like an old-fashioned silent movie. I was frozen to that spot on the branch, and drew my knees up to my chin. I made myself as small as possible, hoping that I had the silhouette of a very large green apple. The D.I. lifted the old gate, forced it back into the gap in the beech hedge, and tied it securely on both sides. I could hear him muttering all the time, but because he had his back towards me, I couldn't make out any of the words.

The D.I. stood for several minutes glaring across the trampled corn field towards the field gate and then he turned, looked straight at the tree where I was hiding, and determinedly marched towards it, picking up the dropped apples on route. I was trapped! My bowels wanted to move, and I fought to keep them under control. But the nervous rumbling of my stomach was like not-too-distant thunder. I could hear my heart pounding, and my breathing was forced and rasping. "He's bound to hear it," I said to myself. It all sounded so loud to me. The D.I. was approaching the tree, still looking down at the ground and occasionally picking up the dropped apples. I wanted to be sick. I started to shake and, then to make matters worse, I began to sob quietly. "My father will kill me, if he finds out and my mother will be so ashamed, how will I ever face them?" My petrified eyes followed the occasional glimpses of the figure through the leaves. He was almost directly beneath me. I held my breath as he passed below, muttering, "Bloody thieving childen!" But, to my astonishment, he just carried on. He kept walking towards the French windows, carrying handfuls of little green apples. When he reached the house he turned round, looked at the tree and then at the gap in the hedge, shook his head ruefully and disappeared into the study, closing the French windows behind him. After a moment the light in the study was switched on, and he came back and looked out into the orchard for the last time. Then pulled the curtains tightly across.

I stayed – unmoving – for a further five minutes, not believing my luck, but shaking like the leaves around me in the gentle warm evening breeze. Nothing had changed in the house, and all seemed to be still. I gently pulled some more apples from the tree and stuffed them into my pockets. With sloth-like movements I slid down to the ground on the opposite side of the tree to the house. I shrank as thin as I could behind the trunk, all the time listening for that angry shout, but it never came. When I sneaked a look at the house, all was silent, so I tiptoed across to the gap in the beech hedge, pausing behind each intermediate tree on route. The gate was securely tied, and I did not want to take the time to free it, so I climbed quickly over.

It was almost completely dark, and I ran through the corn, following one of the dark pathways made by the flight of the ground support team. I climbed the field gate carefully in the dark and found myself in a deserted avenue. Swiftly I made my way back to Command Headquarters, namely our neighbour's garden shed. As I approached I could hear the gang members arguing inside, "We've got to go and rescue him", my brother was shouting. "We're not going back there tonight," retorted the leader, as I pushed open the door. The door creaked as it swung open, and those inside froze. There was a sharp intake of breath, and then they spun round to face me as I sauntered into the light, munching a little green apple.

Their faces lit up with relief. "It's him, he's here," one of my awestruck fellow gang-members whispered hoarsely. "Mr Cool" had arrived with his little green apples! As I shared them out, I told my story, which was far from the truth. I was instantly promoted to a full and much-valued member of the gang. There would be no more of the "Dopey" treatment for me. We chewed on our little green apples, which were as bitter as gall, but we forced them down. We couldn't even smile, our lips were pursed in spasm by the bitterness, but our elation at such a successful raid, against all odds, carried us through the taste-barrier.

Later that night, with a belly full of severe cramps, my head in the toilet bowl one minute and my bottom on it the next, I regretted my foolhardiness. After about an hour the misery stopped and I was able to get into my bed again. I lay for what seemed to be ages before sleep swamped my feelings of nausea, and during that time I was able to reflect on what I had learned.

First, the most important lesson was not to break the law; it wasn't worth the misery of being caught. My mother once told me that there was a time to fight and a time to run away. However, she never got round to telling me which was which, and sometimes I find myself fighting when I feel I should be running away, and vice versa.

Secondly, it taught me that "intelligence" is just another word for information, and it might be either entirely wrong, or the situation may change so rapidly that it becomes useless anyway. We subsequently found out that the D.I. had swapped his evening duty, so that a colleague could attend a social function.

Thirdly, it taught me that fear has a purpose. It heightens the senses and makes one very aware. It also helps you to think and react quickly, and hopefully effectively.

Fourthly, I learnt never to let fear overcome me. Panic dispenses with logic, so common sense cannot come to your rescue. Also, if you smile in the face of adversity, the outcome is usually better.

Lastly, it taught me – *always* – to go to the toilet before going out to do something challenging or important.

The Brass Bed

It was nine-thirty in the evening, on a bitterly cold Christmas Eve and as I left the cottage hospital there was another flurry of snow. I would have to be careful when I got up into the mountains, as I knew that the snow would be lying deeply there. The roads were very slippery, but the snow was only about an inch deep and it didn't cause me any problems. As the Doctor-on-Call, I was driving the "Immediate Care Vehicle". This was a four-wheel drive estate car, which contained all the equipment that a doctor would need to deal with medical emergencies. Thankfully, it also had radio communications with the local ambulance service and my home in case I was the one who ended up needing help.

It took me almost half an hour to reach the patient's home. It was a traditional old Mourne farmhouse with its gable-end to the road. As there was no outside light on at the front of the house, I drove past the end and turned into the large farmyard behind. It was in darkness, but as I parked the car, the back door was flung open and the light spilt out across the yard to welcome me. I had never been to this house before. It belonged to a family who were patients of a colleague of mine, whom I was covering on the rota. I got out of the car, lifted my medical bag from the passenger seat, and turned towards the brightly lit doorway, now almost filled by the dark silhouette of a middle-aged woman.

"Mrs O'Farrell?" I asked tentatively as I walked carefully towards her.

"Oh, it's Doctor McAtier," replied the silhouette. "No, I'm Rita O'Farrell, I look after my mother, Mrs Sinead O'Farrell, and she's the patient," Rita rattled on in a rapid excited voice. "She's in her eighty-eighth year now, you know. I look after her myself, you see, I'm her youngest daughter.'

"That's fine," I said walking into the welcoming warmth of the kitchen and the door was quickly closed behind me. I turned to look at Rita, in the bright light of the kitchen. She was primly dressed in practical dark colours, and over it she was wearing a spotlessly clean floral apron, no doubt changed just for the Doctor's visit. She had a pale, severe yet attractive face, framed by dark greying hair pulled severely into a bun at the back. The close-matching hairnet was easily seen, twinkling in the bright light of the kitchen.

"We live here by ourselves now, the rest of the family have married and moved away and my father died nearly ten years ago just before Easter. It was the Wednesday before Good Friday, God rest his soul!" Rita rattled on. "We buried him on Good Friday and Easter has always been a sad time for us since then." As Rita talked, I was able to take in my surroundings. We were standing in a large kitchen, a sink unit to my left under a window overlooking the farmyard; beyond that was a table against the wall, with three chairs pushed neatly under it. To the right, most of the wall at the far end of the room was taken up with a vast range and as we walked towards it the warmth met me from the roaring fire, visible through the open fire door.

There was a door to the right of the range, which led into the hall. Just before we reached it, I paused to let Rita pass me, so that she could lead the way. There was a steep narrow flight of stairs on the left and Rita headed up them and I followed her. "Mother felt very tired and weak earlier this evening, she has been rushing around too much, you know," Rita continued. "Some of my brothers and sisters, and the grand children are coming tomorrow afternoon, and she wanted to have all their presents sorted out and wrapped for them."

"She still misses my Father very much, especially at Christmas, they always went to Midnight Mass together, so Christmas is both a sad and a happy time for her." Following up the steep staircase behind her, I had a vision, below the longish dark skirt, of shapely legs encased in dark grey heavy stockings, neat ankles and a pair of well-worn floral bedroom slippers. I wondered, was this still the fate of many of the younger daughters of large Irish families? Were they were destined to be spinsters looking after elderly parents, denied the enjoyment of marriage and parenthood?

There was a low beam, but once through the space there was ample head room, and I was able to straighten up when we reached the top of the staircase. We turned left along a corridor, which was triangular in cross-section because of the falling angle of the low roof. "I was a bit worried about mother, being the age she is and it's so good of you to come out to see her on such a night. Isn't it very cold? It's started snowing hard again, so we may have a white Christmas. It'll be the first one for about ten years." Rita chatted away as she paused at a door at the end of the corridor; its strange shape caught my attention. The top had been cut away to follow the descending roof-line so that it was about six feet on the left, hinged side and only about four feet on the right side, where there was an old-fashioned door latch. Rita knocked firmly on the door and asked in a loud voice, "Mother it's the Doctor, Doctor McAtier's here. Is it alright if we come in?"

"Yes, of course you may," the faint reply came from within.

Rita opened the door and stood aside to usher me into the room. As she was standing on the tall side of the door in the narrow corridor, I had to stoop to squeeze past her through the doorway. I was very aware of her closeness and also the pungent aroma, which appeared to be a mixture of mothballs and cheap perfume. "Mother, this is Doctor McAtier," said Rita following me into the room. "He's Doctor Wilson's son-in-law, you know, he's married to his youngest daughter Martha. They live at Ballyardle, not far from where our Pat's Mary comes from." So much for the pedigree, I thought.

The room was long and narrow, the ceiling falling to both sides along the line of the roof. There was a window at the far end, heavily curtained for warmth. Just inside the door to my right was a dressing table in dark wood with a large mirror on the top, and the patient was in a large double bed behind the door. "You're very welcome," said Mrs O'Farrell. She was a smaller and older version of Rita. The hair was exactly the same, the face, although heavily lined had a striking similarity, but she had a prominent jowl hanging down from the firm determined jaw. Her rather scrawny neck disappeared into the high frilled collar of a heavy, blue and white striped winceyette nightdress. Her shoulders were covered by a black woollen shawl, which was drawn tightly across her breast.

"I'll leave you now Doctor. If there is anything you need, give me a call. The Priest is coming to anoint her after he has finished Midnight Mass," Rita said as she rushed out of the bedroom, closing the door firmly behind her. I turned, smiled and walked towards the bed.

"Now I'll just check you over Mrs O'Farrell and see if there are any problems," I said as I swept on to the bed, sitting down heavily on the nearest bottom corner and setting my medical bag down on the bed beside me. It was a large iron bedstead with very decorative brass bed ends, consisting of rows of fine vertical rods, those at each corner, supporting enormous brass balls. They must have been about four inches in diameter.

The unexpected usually catches you out and, it was the construction of the bed that was to cause me concern. The springs of the iron bed frame had worn out many years ago. They had been removed, and a heavy wooden frame with deep new springs had been placed on top of the square metal bed frame. This was prevented from slipping off by four small brass clips, one at each corner. Unfortunately one had broken off, and as I sat down heavily the entire wooden frame rotated on the metal bed frame, and the corner, on which I was sitting, dropped suddenly towards the floor. My "behind" went down with the wooden frame, and as I passed the iron bed frame it caught me behind the knees, shooting my legs into the air and tumbling me backwards across the bed. My medical case tumbled over on top of me and Mrs O'Farrell, wide eyed with surprise, toppled gracefully forwards pushing the bedclothes before her. I was pinned there by her weight and the more I tried to get up, the deeper I pushed the wooden bed frame and the lower I sank. With the medical bag, the bedclothes and Mrs O'Farrell on top of me it was distinctly claustrophobic, and I was aware of an acute pain in one of my most sensitive parts.

When I spoke my voice had a distant, muffled, eerie yet urgent sound to it: "Mrs O'Farrell, could you please try to move your right elbow." The pain in my nether regions eased dramatically. 'Now, could you move up to the top of the bed on the other side?' I asked. The pressure eased gradually, and I was able to push back the bedclothes. The cool air was a welcome relief, and I pulled myself up out of the hollow, rolled off the bed and stood up. I was looking straight into the dressing table mirror and saw looking back at me a very dishevelled, overheated, red-faced, me! I turned to apologise, but a flustered looking Mrs O'Farrell spoke first: "Doctor I'm so sorry. Sure I knew the bed needed to be fixed, it's been unsafe for some time now, but with no man about the house, I was waiting for one of my sons to be here to fix it. Are you all right?"

"Oh I'm all right," I said, somewhat breathlessly, brushing back my hair and straightening my tie and clothing. "More to the point, how are you?"

"I'm grand, sure that was as exciting as the Postman's Knock we used to play at the Christmas Parties in the old days," chuckled Mrs O'Farrell. "But it was as well Rita didn't come in, she's had a sheltered life and wouldn't have understood what was happening." Indeed, I thought to myself, she would have been shocked at what appeared to have been her mother sexually assaulting the doctor.

Having got the bed frames safely sorted out, and the bedclothes tidily rearranged, I opened my medical bag and found the contents were in total disarray from the tumble it had taken. When I had it sorted out, I checked Mrs O'Farrell thoroughly and could not find any life threatening condition, so I reassured her. Advising her to take things easy over Christmas, I gathered my equipment together, put it into the medical bag, picked it up and walked towards the door.

"Well goodnight Mrs O'Farrell, I don't think you'll have any problems, but I'll let your own Doctor know in the morning that I have seen you, and he'll call if he considers it necessary." Just as I was about to open the bedroom door, there was a loud knock and Rita asked if she could come in. "Of course," replied her mother and Rita bustled in. "I've checked your mother over Rita and she fine. Most likely she has been over doing things the last few days, so I've advised her to take things easy for a while," I said knowledgeably.

"Oh she looks so much better because of your visit Doctor,' said Rita, 'sure she's got a really good colour back in her cheeks." I glanced towards Mrs O'Farrell, who returned my look with a mischievous smile. "Goodnight Mrs O'Farrell," I said warmly returning her smile. "Goodnight Doctor, your visit did me an awful lot of good," she replied. "It's been a pleasure,' I responded as I left the bedroom, and followed by Rita started down the steep narrow stairs.

"Watch yourself on the roads tonight Doctor," she said, "it's freezing hard and the snow is getting deeper. It must be nearly four inches deep by now." We were almost half way down the stairs and as I turned to reply my head thudded loudly into the low wooden beam that I had successfully avoided on the way up. I was momentarily dazed and sat down heavily on the stairs, hanging on to the banister with my free hand while holding on tightly to my medical bag with the other. My head was aching and I was seeing stars flashing across in front of my eyes.

"Oh my goodness, are you all right?" Rita cried out. "Yes! Yes!" I answered quickly, although I felt far from all right. "Don't worry Rita, I was endowed with a good thick skull when I was born." I turned round gingerly and gave her, what I hoped, was a reassuring smile, in spite of my throbbing head. "Oh Doctor," said Rita anxiously. "I do hope you are all right, I should have warned you about that beam, we all know about it, but this is your first visit to our home, and it's my fault that I didn't warn you. I'm awfully sorry Doctor."

"Rita, for goodness sake don't blame yourself, I should be old enough to look after myself, it was entirely my fault,' I said. I stood up carefully, ducked under the beam and somewhat unsteadily made my way to the bottom of the stairs. Sitting on the hall table was a small silver tray with a linen tray cloth on it, and votive candles in small silver candlesticks. Rita was ready for the priest's visit to her mother. I hope she warns him about the beam, I thought, and what about her mother's bed? All sorts of pictures flashed through my mind, and then I thought that the sooner I'm out of this house the better, or I'll need the priest more than Mrs O'Farrell. I bid a hasty goodnight and hurried out through the kitchen into the farmyard. It was snowing quite heavily but the cold darkness was almost welcoming and I climbed wearily into the van.

The cold air cleared my head, although it still ached and I had the occasional star flashing across my line of vision. "If I was one of the Wise Men," I muttered to myself, "which one of these stars would I follow on this Christmas Eve?" I started the engine and drove carefully home. To this day, I never precede anyone down a flight of stairs, so that I can see, without distraction, what dangers lurk in my path. Also, if there is someone in front of me, there is always something soft to land on if I should fall! Even a doctor is not immune to the unexpected dangers of daily life.

A Question of Sex

As a rural general medical practitioner I often received gifts throughout the year of "free range" eggs, poultry, fish or vegetables. Although I was grateful for all the gifts, some were exceptional, either because of the pleasure or the hilarity they gave me. One such gift, which I received about twenty-five years ago, gave me both.

It started in mid-December when a farmer's wife, whose seriously ill mother I had been attending, rang me at the surgery. She thanked me for all my efforts and said that she wanted to give me a goose for Christmas. I had very fond memories from my childhood at the end of the Second World War when, with rationing still strictly enforced, it had been difficult to get something "different" for Christmas dinner. My mother, however, had somehow managed to get a goose. She had prepared it carefully and filled it with a sage, onion and breadcrumb stuffing. Then it was roasted slowly, pricked and frequently basted with cider. The aroma of that roasting goose and the exotic flavours of that Christmas meal, especially the gravy, live on in my mind to this present day. My mother even collected and stored the goose fat, to treat bruises and sprains sustained in the rough and tumble of adolescent life. It certainly helped, although with its particularly strong obnoxious smell everyone knew that I was under treatment and I usually spent a considerable amount of convalescence on my own.

With all these memories buzzing in my mind, I readily accepted the generous offer of the goose, and arranged that it would be delivered to my home a short time before Christmas. Arriving home for my lunch, after my morning rounds, I announced the good news to my wife, only to be informed that we already had another offer of a turkey for Christmas. She suggested however, that we could freeze the goose and keep it for another occasion. After all my lovely memories of previous goose dinners I was slightly disappointed but at least it would happen some time in the near future.

With only a few days to go before Christmas, my wife and I arranged to go to Belfast for a last round up of presents and food and drink requirements. My eldest son David was home from boarding school and would look after the younger children and the house. We warned him that the goose might be delivered, and that he should hang it from a hook in one of the roof joists at the back of the garage. It was a long frenetic day of pondering and decision-making and it was cold and dark when we arrived home exhausted from Belfast and we were eagerly greeted by the family. David gave us a report of their day, the incoming phone calls and visitors at the door as well as descriptions of what they had been up to.

"By the way a young man came with the goose and I opened the garage and he hung it up on the hook for me," he added.

"Did he hang it up by the neck or the feet?" my wife enquired. "It should be hung by the feet so that the bruising will drain into the head and neck and won't discolour the flesh in the breast."

"I don't know mum," David replied. "It was in a sack!"

"Oh well don't worry, your Dad will check it when he puts the cars in the garage after supper."

Supper was prepared and when young inquisitive eyes were otherwise engaged the "gifts" from Santa Claus and the foodstuffs were secretly brought into the house. Then when all were tidied away and supper was finished I went out to put the car in the garage. My mind was full of the thoughts of Christmas and whether we had got everything we needed for the day. I can remember seeing a sack hanging from the beam, about eighteen inches in front of the windscreen when I stopped the car. However, I forgot all about what I was supposed to do and I shut the garage door, locked it and hurried into the house, out of the cold frosty night.

My wife was in the frenetic process of trying to get three excited boys into bed but when she finally came down into the sitting room she asked, "What about the goose?" I sheepishly had to admit that I hadn't looked and got up to go out to check it. However, she took pity on me and with a bemused smile and a shake of her head she said, "Don't worry, it won't take any harm until the morning."

There had been a heavy frost through the night and everywhere was white when we awoke the next morning. After breakfast, as I was going to get the cars out of the garage, my wife pointedly told me, "Make sure you check the goose!" This time, before I closed the garage door, I walked over to the sack hanging from the beam and grasped it to lift it off the hook. "Hiss, hissss, hissssss!!!" went the sack and it began to wriggle so violently that I had to put it down quickly on the floor in case I dropped it. The goose inside was very much alive; it had obviously managed to get a foot into each lower corner of the sack for it staggered off towards the doorway. Before it could escape I caught up with the "walking sack", lifted it by the large knot, which had been tied in the top, rotated it through one hundred and eighty degrees and set it down again. The sack set off again and wobbled back into the garage and I quickly pulled down the up-and-over door. I stood in the cold, wide eyed, startled and confused but thinking furiously as to how I could address the problem.

When I had my mind somewhat organised I hurried back into the house. My wife, who at that stage, was tidying up the breakfast dishes, looked up at me, smiled and asked, "Well, how did you find the goose this morning?"

"Hmm," I responded. "We have a bit of a problem with the goose."

"Oh dear, don't tell me it hasn't been cleaned out?" as the smile faded from her face.

"Well, it's a bit worse than that dear."

"Don't tell me that it's not even plucked either?" she said looking a bit perplexed.

"It's even worse than that I'm afraid."

"What do you mean?" she asked and then an expression of concerned realisation appeared on her face. "It's not still alive is it?"

"Yes, I'm afraid it is," I replied, "and it's still in the sack and wandering around our garage!"

"Oh my goodness!" she exclaimed as she rushed towards the back door with me in full pursuit. "The poor thing, spending all night hung up in that sack."

"Well, it was really just like a sailor sleeping in a hammock," I replied somewhat defensively.

When we arrived at the front of the garage, I gingerly raised the door and the sack was sitting motionless against the back of the garage. The noise of the opening door attracted its attention and the sack rose on its corners and wobbled towards us, the large knot, on the top, bobbing from side to side. My wife, startled by the apparition, sidestepped the advancing sack, dodged behind me as I lifted it, again rotating it, so that when I put it down, it set off back into the garage once more. I followed it, and every time it came to an obstacle, I lifted and rotated it through ninety degrees. The sack and I were now proceeding in an orderly fashion, "goose-stepping" around in a square in the garage. As I proceeded, I was holding a deep discussion with my wife as to what we should do.

"Now that I've seen it alive, I couldn't have it killed," she said determinedly.

"But you haven't seen it yet, it's still in the sack!" I responded indignantly.

"Oh but I know it's alive and I'm sure it's a really beautiful goose," she said emphatically as we marched across in front of her. My anticipation of a savoury goose dinner was fast receding from my mind.

"Fine, but what do you do with a live goose three days before Christmas?"

"Well, we could keep it and feed it until we could find it a suitable home," she replied emphatically. However, the liberal use and emphasis of the "Royal We" made me a bit apprehensive as to who would be doing the "looking after".

"We've never kept fowl here before, where on earth will we house it and where do I get the right food for it?" I asked as I sped on my way, becoming quite dizzy going round and round in circles in such a confined space. "Who do we know that keeps geese anyway?" I panted.

"Well there's the Community at the top of the road which has a farm," my wife replied.

"That's the first good suggestion you've made. I know that they definitely had geese; I used to see them in their orchard. They used them to guard the apple trees in the autumn from the local lads. I seem to remember though, that they told me they'd lost them. They were either stolen, or the foxes got them. Could you give them a ring and see if they could accommodate our friend here?" I asked. "I would do it but I somehow feel you'd rather not be left alone with our marching sack."

She was off like a shot and I spent another five minutes "goose-stepping" until she came back with a broad happy smile on her face. "I was talking to Klaus and they'd be delighted to take our goose," she said happily. "They only have one goose left, the foxes got the others about three months ago. By the way he asked me what sex it was, so I told him that I didn't know because it was still in a sack. He said to bring it up to them anyway and they would sort something out."

I had known Klaus for many years; he was the most senior "House Parent" in the Community. "That's great," I said picking up the sack and putting it into the back of my wife's station wagon. "I'll take it up right now and resolve the matter once and for all."

The "Ulster Troubles" were at their worst around this time, and as I drove carefully up the road I glanced in the rear-view mirror. I could see over the back seat and there was a bobbing knot going round in circles in the rear of the car. It was one of those classic "What if" moments. What if I was stopped at a security force roadblock? What would the security forces think of my "walking sack"? However, I arrived safely at my destination and found Klaus waiting for me beside the orchard accompanied by their sole surviving goose, which was waddling up and down inside the orchard fence honking furiously at being disturbed.

"Have you had a look at it yet?" asked Klaus as I lifted the sack out of the back of the car. I set it on the ground and replied as I untied the knot. "No, this is just as it arrived with us." I tipped the sack over and out slid a beautiful white goose. It stood up, stretched its head high and began to honk in unison with the other goose in the orchard. "Do you know what sex it is?" I asked Klaus.

"Don't ask me, I haven't got a clue. They all look the same to me," he replied with a wry smile.

"Well the only way to find out is to put them together and see what happens," I suggested, as I opened the gate in the orchard fence, and the two of us shepherded the indignant goose through it into the potential battlefield. The two geese approached each other warily and then circled each other honking furiously.

"Do you know what sex your goose is?" I asked Klaus tentatively.

"Again, as I said, I haven't got a clue," he replied concentrating on the circling geese.

"Well I only hope the geese can work it out," I whispered apprehensively, afraid to disturb the intensity of what was happening in front of us. The two geese had now stopped circling each other, the honking had stopped and they were getting closer and closer. There was some tentative beak tapping which then progressed into neck rubbing, then there appeared to be a bit of goose chatting and then they both turned round to stare disdainfully at the two anxious humans peering apprehensively over the fence. Their body language and disconcerting stare seemed to say, "What a palaver you ignorant humans have put us through, when we could, so easily, sort it out by ourselves."

"They must be the opposite sex!" I exclaimed triumphantly.

"Maybe only time will tell," said Klaus. "You know, I still can't see any difference."

I hurried home to break the good news to my waiting family, and one might assume that such a happy ending would bring the matter to an appropriate closure, but the story continued. On Christmas Eve my wife went to the Bank. It was crammed with people and the queue was like a snake winding its way backwards and forwards, as the busy staff processed the customers. Further forward in the queue was Klaus and when my wife was passing him there was a sudden spontaneous lull in the buzz of conversation, just as he said loudly, "Funny your husband didn't know about the sex!" You could have heard a pin drop in the stunned silence.

"Well of course it's not really his field of expertise," my wife replied loudly, sensing that an amusing situation was developing. The queue moved on separating her from Klaus and the conversation exploded only to abruptly become silent again when Klaus and my wife were again beside each other on different coils of the snake.

"I thought a man of his experience would have been able to tell," Klaus said loudly as he also now realised the intense and focused interest around him.

"Well, I suppose if it was something he was involved in every day he would have known right away," my wife responded.

As the queue moved on the buzz of conversation rose again. But it had become generally quieter; people were beginning to form into little groups, heads together, whispering out of the corners of their mouths while casting covert glances at Klaus and my wife. They were gauging when they had to switch to a strict listening mode in order not to miss the next instalment of the developing saga. When the next meeting of the ways occurred, all movement and conversation ceased, even people at the front of the queue didn't want to go to the counter in case they missed one word.

"My husband thought that at least you would know about the sex as you deal with these things all the time," my wife again spoke loudly, playing to the attentive audience.

"Well the happy couple seem to be working it out but we'll just have to give them time and space to see what the final outcome will be," Klaus responded.

"As long as there are no ructions and the relationship doesn't get too physical, it should be all right," responded my wife as the queue again moved on. Customers who had already been dealt with were rejoining the queue, talking animatedly to friends in order to hear the final episode, soon it would be Klaus's turn to go forward to the counter and that might be the end of the saga. However, when the encounter took place again and the conversation died away, Klaus turned to the silent expectant crowd and with a broad smile said loudly, "I'm awfully sorry to disappoint you but we were talking about a pair of geese. Happy Christmas everyone!" There was a loud outburst of laughter, the buzz of conversation rose once again but it was relieved, happy, generous and full of the spirit of Christmas.

The pair of geese lived happily together in the Community's orchard. My Christmas goose befriended Klaus's son and used to follow him around like a dog, much to the amusement of community members and visitors alike. 'It' turned out to be a 'she', who laid a copious number of eggs and reared successive generations of goslings. I know she had a long, fruitful and happy life, but I never wanted to know if she ended up as someone else's savoury goose dinner. I'd like to think that she died peacefully in her sleep of old age. However, I now realise that when I tipped her out of the sack it was a really defining moment in her life, because her future depended on "A Question of Sex".

A Funereal Farce

Joe was a quiet philosophical man. Indeed he wouldn't have survived so long if he hadn't been. He had a club foot, which had left him with a marked, permanent limp and very much limited in what he could do in life as a working-class lad. In the end, he had found his ideal job working behind the bar in the local hotel. It was ideal because he did not have to walk too far, few noticed his disability behind the bar, and they normally talked among themselves, allowing him to get on with his job. He was happy and contented with his work, although it didn't pay much, and the hours were long and unsociable. Still, he had a job and felt more of a man through being able to work.

Joe had married Mary Ellen forty-five years ago. It had been a small quiet wedding, they were both "only children" and their parents were elderly and frail. Money was scarce and they couldn't afford a large reception, and neither of them wanted a crowd. Joe, because of his disability, was sensitive and shy. Mary Ellen was also quiet, having worked since she left school at sixteen, as her Ladyship's personal maid in the "Big House" in the park.

The speeches at the small reception were thankfully short, although some jokingly referred to the prospect of the "patter of tiny feet around the house". This had provoked loud and embarrassed laughter at the time, but as the years rolled by without any sign of a family, such remarks became more of an irritation than an embarrassment. Apart from Joe's disability, they were healthy enough and enjoyed a warm physical relationship. Sadly, however, Mary Ellen never became pregnant. Although they talked in private about the lack of a family, they were shy about it, and didn't seek advice or medical help until they were in their forties. Then the many tests and the complexity of the treatment, with its potential complications, were so distasteful that they decided that they wouldn't bother any more. They had each other and that was enough for both of them.

"If only" is so easy to say in hindsight, for in her sixty-third year Mary Ellen found, what all women dread to find, a lump in her breast. She went into denial and didn't mention it to Joe, hoping and praying that it would go away. She convinced herself it was something harmless, and nothing to worry about. But it grew larger and became painful, and by the time she had plucked up courage to mention it to Joe, it had spread into her armpit. Joe was stunned and angered by the news. How could she have let something, so threatening to their lives together, intrude so far and not share it with him? They went to see their doctor and were immediately referred to the Breast Clinic at their nearest acute hospital. Mary Ellen was admitted as an emergency and operated on the following day. In spite of the extensive major surgery, followed by very unpleasant chemotherapy, the cancer spread relentlessly, and Mary Ellen began to deteriorate steadily.

When it had become obvious that Mary Ellen was not going to survive, Joe had retired from his job so that he could be with her. He was devoted to her and with the help of attendants, nurses and doctors, he was able to look after her at home. Mary Ellen realised that because of her, Joe was becoming housebound and insisted that he should get a little dog for company. It would encourage him to go out for walks. He was easily convinced and got in touch with one of his old regular customers from the bar who, he knew, bred Jack Russell terriers. He had a young dog available, and would gladly sell it to Joe.

The little dog was friendly, cheerful and active. He was mostly white with a large black patch around his rump and tail, two other small black patches around each ear, and a large golden brown patch around and across his shoulders. Mary Ellen and Joe discussed names at length and eventually decided to call the dog "Crisps" because Joe said that his old customer, who had sold him the dog, was always munching crisps at the bar.

As Mary Ellen deteriorated and became bed-bound, the little dog became Joe's constant companion. Crisps went everywhere with him and, as Mary Ellen had hoped, got him out of the house. The pair became a familiar sight around the town. Joe limping laboriously along behind an eager, scrabbling Crisps, on the end of a very taut lead. In the end Mary Ellen slipped away just before her sixty-fifth birthday. A home without a woman can be a cold and lonely place and, like most men, Joe had no housekeeping skills. With the love of his life gone, in spite of the home helps, the house began to become dark and depressing, and no love or pride remained.

The walks that Joe and Crisps had so enjoyed became less frequent and they spent longer in front of the television beside the fire. But whereas Crisps still got his tinned dog food to eat and a good run around the garden afterwards, Joe's diet consisted of an unhealthy mix of junk food washed down with beer or stout, and he took no exercise at all. His weight increased remarkably, and with his very low activity the inevitable happened. One night he took a severe coronary and although hospitalised rapidly he died soon afterwards. It was almost two years since Mary Ellen had passed away, and because there were now no living relatives, their friends and the parish made all Joe's funeral arrangements.

Graveyards are never anything but bleak, even in summer, but in the middle of November, with a biting east wind swirling around the headstones, it was forbidding. The open grave is always a fearful portal to the next world. There were only a few mourners standing around the grave, and they were wrapped up in various layers of wool, topped by heavy coats with scarves and gloves. The mourners pitied the poor priest, his face pinched and pale white in the cold. His vestments swirled around him, ballooning outwards and upwards showing off his polished shoes, black socks and black trousers without turn-ups. He still hadn't bought himself a new suit, but they hoped he had taken the time to put on his thermal underwear. He needed it, at that graveside.

With the coffin lowered, the pallbearers retreated, pulling their gloves on over cold stiff fingers. The little dog Crisps was at the graveside to see his old master off. He was on a lead of course, held by his new master. The priest began the prayers, droning on in an unsubtle monotone, while the wind gusted and swirled, again ballooning the priest's vestments outwards and upwards. Crisps was particularly interested in the priest's lamp-post-like legs, especially the shiny black shoes which had a strong farmyard aroma. He suddenly lifted his leg and before anyone could react, he peed on the unsuspecting priest. The warm amber fluid ran down his trouser leg and because there were no turn-ups, it sped rapidly in its spread down the black sock and into the black polished shoe.

Everybody knows that dogs have a higher body temperature than humans, and the priest, suffering in the cold wind and unaware of the cause, temporarily enjoyed the feeling of warmth in his shoe. The mourners beside and behind the priest had seen what had happened, the lead was jerked and Crisps was pulled aside. Mischievous smiles appeared on their faces, some struggled to contain themselves, and some giggled out loud. The priest thankfully didn't notice, as he was concentrating deeply. Reaching the climax of his graveside duties, he intoned, 'Earth to earth, ashes to ashes, dust to dust'. The undertaker threw the handfuls of earth and pebbles into the grave, and Crisps wanted to chase them as they rattled on the top of his old master's coffin. He was restrained by another sharp tug on the lead, began to bark stridently and was quickly led away.

The grave was covered and as there were no relatives present with whom to sympathise, the mourners quickly began to disperse. The priest battled his way against the wind back to the church to divest himself of his vestments. He was surprised how his one warm foot was now becoming cold, and when he checked, he was even more surprised to find that the outside of the leg of his trousers was soaking wet, as was the outside of his sock. When he had taken off his robes he removed his shoe and squelched over to the wash-hand basin. Taking one of the paper towels he proceeded to dry out the shoe, noting the strong smell of ammonia but shrugging off any suspicions in his mind. As he placed the shoe on top of a radiator he decided that the pile of rotting leaves he had walked through at the side of the church must have concealed a large puddle of rancid water. Rinsing his sock in the wash-hand basin, he made up his mind to get the puddle cleared away.

Crisps had escaped any ecclesiastical wrath; even possible Excommunication and he would be allowed to visit his late master's grave without restrictions. The priest hung his sock over a radiator beside his shoe, deciding that he would draft out next Sunday's sermon while he waited for them to dry. What would his text be? The mourners could have suggested to him – 'Every dog has its day'!

BERNADETTE BECKETT

The Opera-Singing Electrician

Picture a boy in the small streets of Belfast, lounging in the entry, with a Marlon Brando white cotton vest, Brylcreemed hair and a hard-man attitude to match. He'd been scrawny and sickly as a child, and cosseted by an anxious mother. As a teenager, he built up his muscles using a course from an American magazine, and many years later would tease his nine children with a favourite joke about the customer who writes back to the Charles Atlas body-building company: *Course completed, please forward muscles.*

When he left school at fourteen his mother sat beside him in St Finian's School, at an interview with the Head Brother. Uncertainty about his future hung in the air, and they discussed his options. When the brother stood to conclude the interview, he announced cheerily: "Not to worry. With a name like Alex Johnston, you'll never be stuck for a job in the shipyard." This Protestant-sounding name was to guarantee Daddy employment, and physical safety in that employment, for many years. He worked all over Northern Ireland. Over the years, on many a Sunday outing, we'd pass a roundabout with tall sodium lights and he'd say: "I wired those lights when I worked for such and such a company in such and such a year." His favourite remark was: "If you're in the Royal Victoria Hospital on the operating theatre and the electricity goes off, don't worry, your oul fella wired the emergency generator, and you'll come to no harm."

Daddy always said that his own 'oul fella' claimed to have met Marconi and he recently discovered that it must be true. He had begun to investigate his family tree and found my Grandfather's discharge papers from the Great War. He was a telegraphist, which is a job, and therefore a word, we no longer need. After the war, he worked for the Post Office and he was present on the day when Marconi sent a test radio signal from Ballycastle to Rathlin Island. A handsome monument commemorating this historic event stands near the harbour in Ballycastle harbour to this day.

Daddy had a store of marvellous funny and sad stories from his days as an electrician in a series of firms, from the Fifties to the Nineties. They were stories of wonderful men of every slant and style, including chancers, dodgers, gentlemen, poets, drunks, cowards, family men, bigots, lechers – and they all respected Daddy. He had a best friend whom he'd known since childhood and had worked with him for many years. One day Daddy got a phone call to say that his old friend was dead. He had been shot in a mysterious incident in north Belfast. This man had been deeply involved in the IRA and in all those years of friendship and closeness, Daddy had never known about it.

He used to tell a story of a plumber friend who'd worked in the shipyard. One day he dropped a hammer and cracked a bath while fitting out a luxury ship. He panicked about losing his job and needing to get rid of the evidence, he smashed up the rest of the bath and dropped it, piece by piece, out of the porthole. Later, when the inspectors came round to carry out a check, they scratched their head over two problems: first, how this cabin was missed-out in the original fitting, and secondly, how they were going to get another bath in, now that the narrow doors and gangways had been built around it.

Daddy quoted Shakespeare when he was in good form. 'Oft times on the Rialto' was one of his favourites. We'd exchange looks and roll our eyes with good humour and I now wonder how he became so learned. His knowledge of flora and fauna was excellent and with no pressure and no sense that he was trying to influence us, he would name the little flowers and point out the butterflies. We learnt by picking up on his passion. We also acquired a great knowledge and love of our home country. Only when I was an adult and exposed to the wider world did I realise that other people did not have this knowledge of natural history and Irish geography. I often wondered how I'd emerged from my grammar school experiences with less real education than him.

He'd gone through a 'Rockabilly phase' as a single man, slicking his hair, and trying to look tough, and he never quite got over it. He had a leather jacket, a jerkin he called it, with fringes on the sleeves and a fine red stripe lining the pockets and cuffs. He couldn't give it up. It became his work coat, worn when tinkering with motorbikes, lying under cars. He still wore it when it was falling apart, when it was ripped and oil- spattered, and had moulded into the shape of his stocky body.

I have inherited his height, or lack of it, his humour, his love of music, good books and drawing, but especially his love of music. Daddy explored every new sound before it was fashionable, and he had a collection of eclectic LPs that included rock, classical, opera, banjo twanging country, black American blues, traditional Irish, but usually obscure sounds that no one but music buffs had heard of. When he was relaxed, he sang in a beautiful tenor voice, and he ranged from opera and ballads, to Buddy Holly or the Beatles. In his forties he said to me, "Bernadette, I'm a young man trapped in an old man's body." Now I know that we all feel like this.

He told me this story about his childhood only recently. The River Blackstaff, known as the Blackie, flowed deep and powerful behind the streets near Broadway on the Falls Road, where he lived. Adjacent to this area was the Willowbank Park. The older children hacked at the fence to make a 'crawl hole' to the river bank. The council patched it up. The children opened it again. He was playing nearby when some boys ran up to him shouting: "Help! We need a big boy. There is a child in the river." He ran to the bank to see an infant aged about two, well out in the deep water and lying face down. Daddy pulled him out, and although suspecting he was already dead, he shielded the smaller ones from the sight and told them to run and get Mr. McCann, the only person for miles around who owned a car. This man worked shifts and he was in bed, but was roused and came hurriedly, shuffling along in his bedroom slippers and tucking in his shirt. He took the little body to the Royal. There was a tiny article in the paper the next day but no police, no statement, no questions, no counselling. Daddy was only eleven years old, and the Blackie now runs in a pipe underground.

Daddy could fix anything. When I was five or six and we lived in a council estate there was a constant stream of kettles, televisions and irons in the house for repair. Mummy would nag him, because he wouldn't take money for fixing them. People gave us biscuits and gifts instead, but we badly needed the cash. This was also the era when no one in the street had a car but us, and ours was the taxi which acted for the whole area. Daddy did the runs to the casualty department of the local hospital, ferrying with every feverish infant, or one with a broken leg or split head.

One of my fondest memories is of the start of the school day. The sirens would sound in the local factories to bring the men into work, one at five to eight and another at eight o'clock. This was our cue to get up. Daddy would be in the kitchen by then, ready to leave, but he had made a huge pot of porridge. He poured it into the seven or eight dishes which he then placed in a row on the windowsill. He would open the window to cool the scalding cereal, and the steam would mist the glass. My memory is of the comfort of knowing that security, and knowing that someone was up before me, that the house was warm on a bitter winter morning and, that food was ready. All of this eased me into the day.

It was always Daddy who went out with the torch when you heard something creepy at night, always Daddy who rigged up a light from the car battery and who cooked over the gas camping stove when there was a power failure. It was Daddy who ended up with his hands covered in mud and grime unblocking a pipe or digging a ditch, but whose hands were equally deft in a bowl of flour, baking the Hallowe'en apple cakes with hidden pennies in tin foil.

In our next house when we moved to the dizzy heights of home ownership, he installed the central heating single-handedly, but it took months. He worked an hour here and an hour there, mostly in the evenings. I remember this as a time of absence when the 'Boiler House' became his domain. You'd find him there with the radio on, in overalls, with oily hands, and with his music and a quiet smile.

I have seen less of him of late. He retired from the local brewery where he worked a few years ago, just in time to avoid witnessing its sad demise. It has lately been sold to a foreign conglomerate and stripped piece by piece of its contents, the brew house, the bottling plant, every boiler and beer tank, every vessel and vat, every kettle and keg, the pipes and pumps, the pasteuriser which held six miles of bottles, the beautiful computerised laser printer which marked 'best before' dates, the shiny copper mash tuns with their brass rivets shone to gold after every brew. Daddy would hate to have seen all his handiwork, all his 'babies', carried out the door, and sold to the highest bidder.

I have only begun to kiss my father's precious cheek in the last year or two. Such affection was always felt but was not demonstrated in our house. After he retired, such is the demand for his quality workmanship amongst his family and friends that he has never been busier and, just to be on the safe side, he takes a boiler suit and tool box with him wherever he goes. "Just in case…" The opera-singing electrician is a very special man indeed.

The Roaring Forties

How short our memories are about child rearing! If one more well-meaning person at the supermarket checkout had said to me: 'Enjoy them; they're the best days of your life,' I'd have strangled them. Have these people forgotten the hard bits? The sleep deprivation and endless exhaustion that cause life to take on an unreal quality, when everything is difficult and you're bogged down with responsibility, yet time is fast forwarding. The social life you can't have because you can't get a babysitter? You look back a while later and realise it's as if you've missed it. You're not really *in* the experience as you're having it.

When asked now about the age at which one of my children walked/talked/sat up, I have absolutely no idea. I have recorded it all in their little memories books and I'm so glad I did, because the experience is a blur. And now when the children ask me to play with them, to do a painting or bake some buns, I say, "No, I'm too busy." I'm doing all the extra things I have to do because I have children . . .

Perhaps I'm just not a natural mother. I am too aware of all the sacrifices involved. I'm also a bit of a late developer, and feel that I only arrived at some sort of maturity later than most people, so here I am wanting to do all sorts of creative things that I've postponed for years and now, when I've a clearer idea of what I want, I'm in the throes of raising kids.

I am also conscious that my energy levels are definitely falling. This is bad timing, but it couldn't be helped. I recommend having babies before you reach your forties. Maturity might be on your side, but the downturn in energy levels is a definite disadvantage. My husband and I look on in horrified fascination when we hear about other parents talking about nights out. 'Lights out' is in our vocabulary, but 'nights out'? The expression 'going on somewhere afterwards' referring to a drinking session where you move from the original premises – no, I don't think so. I like to boogie with the best of them but dinner followed by a visit to a – I can hardly frame the word – a club. It's mind-boggling.

I've read articles in which the writer warns the unwary about how "The books won't tell you about how difficult child-rearing can be" but the books I read, *did* tell you. The problem is that they can't possibly do justice to the experience. It's a good example of a life event that must be experienced first hand. Like most life-changing experiences we cannot imagine it, or empathise truly, until we've done it. When child rearing, it is as if you step off the planet and are transported into a new world where you leave pleasures, certainties, hobbies and social life behind.

Your world shrinks and becomes centred on the next feed, bottle, *pooh*, health visit or vaccination, or how much sleep you might get that night. Other lucky people seem to be living in some faraway world, irrelevant but full of allure, meeting for drinks, running businesses, painting pictures, doing degrees, shopping, enthusing or agonising over outfits, hairstyles or where to go on holiday, all trivial yet strangely attractive. How much of this is sleep deprivation is hard to tell.

I remember being in hospital after one of the boys was born. A girl in the same ward was packing to go home the day after giving birth. She pulled the curtains to change and emerged in a size ten clingy Lycra dress, explaining loudly to the rest of us that she had no patience with these frumpy women who allowed a new baby to dominate and ruin their lives. She had no intention of stopping all her usual partying, and she was going to be the same fun-loving person as before. "Good luck my dear," I thought, darkly.

I am awakened at 6.15am and have been up four times during the night. A little person is in my bedroom – no, make that two little people. One is on the floor at the bottom of my bed running a tractor along the new cream rug. It has horizontal stripes which conveniently double as rills. This 'field' is ploughed, sown, fertilised and harvested every few days. I am warned not to step on it when getting out of bed, in a scathing tone that suggests that he wouldn't put such imbecilic behaviour past a city slicker like me.

Child number two is poking a train into my eyes, making 'choo choo' noises to simulate a steam engine, and asking if I am ready to go on board, because Santa is ready to leave. He hopes I've been good, that I've written my list and sent it up the chimney and, oh here is child number three now wearing a London bobby helmet from the dressing up box and carrying a notebook and pencil borrowed from my study. He announces firmly that if I don't co-operate I'll be arrested, and demands to know what meal I want to order. I mutter that I'll have a tuna baguette, only to be told that they aren't on today. I try another tack. "Have you any paninis?" I ask.

"Yes," he replies. "We have them."

"Right, I'll have one of those with bacon and brie."

No. That won't be possible. I can have one with jam, onion and spaghetti bolognese. Wearily I agree. What would I like to drink? I'll have a pot of tea for one please. No, that won't be possible either. Coffee then? "No, they don't sell that. They have cola or beer." This is announced very firmly by a three-year-old with a look and tone that would scare the Maitre'd who lectures in the snobby Maitre'd college. I concede that this meal will do very nicely thank you .and yes of course I'd be delighted to finish with profiteroles with extra strawberry sauce, purple jelly and a sherbet lolly. What am I doing with my life?

I am, as you may have guessed, a mature lady, well travelled and of no mean intelligence, I think. I have *taught* assertiveness courses, for goodness sake. Yet I lie here in awe of the total single-minded determination, confidence and energy of my three-year-old son. I am defeated by it. Do they learn that you cave in out of sheer weariness?

I endure all this and a further barrage of questions and requests, whilst trying to decide how long I can stay in bed without risking missing the school bus, deciding what I'm going to wear to work, whether there is change in my purse for the school dinners and swimming, whether I need a shower or can put my hair up in a knot and make it last one more day without washing, if I have to stop for petrol or whether this means I'll run late in rush hour traffic, whether I have the time and ingredients to rustle up a sandwich for the younger child to take to the child minder's (because I can't send anything from the freezer because he's going to playgroup first and the lunch will be in his bag all morning), whether it's going to be hot enough outside to warrant throwing in the sun cream and if it's not hot, will they need their long trousers?

Then there's the note for teacher to tell her I'll be picking a child up early tomorrow for the opticians and oh, yes, that reminds me, I must change that speech therapist's appointment because it clashes with the Open Day at work and although I don't usually work Thursdays I'm going in this week. Then there's dinner, and I can leave out some prawns and they'll be thawed in time, and oh yes I must remind my husband to get the car taxed. Oh, and I need to take an extra antibiotic today because I forgot to take last night's because I was busy writing the letter of objection to the Planning Office about the new hotel and golf course being built ninety metres from our beautiful rural idyll, a house into which we've just poured our life savings. And that reminds me, the credit card bill needs paid – what date is this anyway? Well, it's due some time soon and I don't want to be paying interest.

Someone asked me the other day why I was always so tired. I threw my head back and gave a maniacal laugh that would have done Christopher Lee proud, then fixed her with a scalpel-like stare (icy corneas and a bit loonie round the whites) and said, "Tired? Who? Me?" Then I muttered, "No, I've just been a bit busy this week."

However, when I look into the three little pairs of grey, dark blue and baby blue eyes I do understand that I've never done anything as wonderful, as special, as important as having these babies, and that I'm lucky to have had them, so easily and so healthily too, all in my Forties. When I screech at them I wish I was one of these paragons of patience who are always loving and calm (is anyone under these circumstances?) instead of the nagging fishwife that I've turned into. My life has become 'The Roaring Forties' but I wouldn't change it for the world.

PAT HEANEY

First Steps to Paradise

My parents were expecting me to do well at school, having labelled me as the clever one of the family in the way parents often seem to enjoy categorizing their offspring, as the 'pretty', or 'talented' one, or the 'practical' one. However, my desperate, personal ambition was to emulate my two older sisters and get a boyfriend, as soon as possible. My sisters appeared to be having a wonderful time, as far as I could see, going off to dances, and meeting up with groups of boys. A boyfriend of my own seemed to be what my life lacked, entirely. It was the one acquisition that would enhance my mundane life, I decided. I was tired of being told that I was too young to go here, or do this, or do that.

At school, I often overheard more knowing classmates discuss their love lives and tease each other about some boy or other. Through regular eavesdropping, I learned that most weekends these girls seemed to go out with the sole intention of meeting potential partners. Afterwards, they would talk loudly of their successes and boast about their conquests to the rest of the class, most of whom, like me, lacked any romantic experience. As far as I could discern, they weren't too worried what the boy looked like, within reason. The important things to them seemed to be that he was male, of a certain age and good at kissing.

I envied them their sophistication. They knew several boys and were able to talk about such mysterious activities as 'French-kissing,' whatever that was. I admired their air of authority and I was deeply jealous of them. Unfortunately, my parents seemed to expect me to spend all of my weekends studying, which ruled out any opportunity for me to have a social life, never mind a boyfriend.

At that time, I knew very few people of the opposite sex, apart from brothers, cousins and their friends and none of these friends lived up to any of my romantic ideals. Nevertheless, in my desperation, I drew up a mental list of them. Any boys I knew well enough to say 'Hello' to, found their way onto the list. On my way to school, some mornings, I would ponder whether to drop any of their names into casual conversations, just to let the others think that I had some experience in the art of love but, at the last moment, I would back away from such boastings, afraid that some clever girl would be able to wheedle out of me how little I *did* know.

The first dance I was given permission to attend was a Ceilidh, in our local town hall, shortly after my fifteenth birthday. Although I was very excited, I was also nervous and slightly dreading the whole night. My friends and I hurried down the hill to the venue, for we were anxious to get inside to view the young men who would be there. My friends had instructed me to act nonchalantly and appear not to be interested in any of the boys, for fear I might embarrass myself or them. As a complete novice in such matters, I was confused by these instructions, but submitted to my friends' superior wisdom.

To my utter humiliation, I was wearing a pale blue, knitted suit, with a pleated skirt. Underneath the jacket was a pink, cotton blouse, sporting a Peter-Pan collar. Now, I had intended to borrow something more stylish and modern from one of my sisters but, unfortunately, since I was taller and heavier than either of them, I was reduced to wearing a suit that had been bought for me the previous Easter, a garment that I now considered much too childish-looking. I was dreading my friends' comments, or even worse, their silent glances of pity. Luckily, for my recent birthday, my parents had given me a fashionable tan bucket bag, which I swung bravely from my left shoulder, hoping to distract people from looking too closely at what I was wearing.

When we ascended the stairs to the ballroom where the Ceilidh was being held, I was horrified to see my father smiling over at me and making his way, guitar in hand, onto the stage. I thought furiously to myself that I should have guessed something of the sort, when my parents had agreed so readily to my request. Although I knew my father played in a band, I just had not thought I would be unfortunate enough to have him playing at my first ever adult event.

Following my friends, my legs heavy with dejection, to the side of the room where other girls and women had already assembled, I could make out untidy knots of men, of different ages and shapes, some of them leaning against the opposite wall, several pairs of eyes scrutinising us. I felt, simultaneously, frightened, excited and self-conscious. I panicked that no one would choose to ask me to dance, especially in my awful powder-blue outfit. Then my heart pumped quickly and loudly even more, when I thought about what I should do if someone did ask me onto the dance-floor.

Luckily, when the music started up, some older people began organising us into sets of eight, four females and four males in each group, as far as they could. The choice of dance partners had been taken out of the young men's hands. I was relieved to be selected into the same set as one of my friends. For that moment, anyway, I didn't care what my partner looked like. I began to understand why looks didn't matter. I was thrilled to be dancing, not standing alone, isolated from everyone.

The older dancers in the group helped the less experienced dancers and, after a short while, I began to enjoy myself, even when we had the occasional muddle as we tried out unfamiliar movements and steps. Very quickly, I forgot about my original nervousness. I was no longer bothered about trying to impress anyone.

When there was an interval, I slipped over to the far side of the hall where a table, selling soft drinks, had been set up. I was looking about for my friends, when a young man from our dancing group came over to me and offered to buy me a lemonade. Although my face blazed with embarrassment, I was thrilled. Imagine, me being bought a drink by a boy! The night was going much better than I had dared to hope.

By the time we had exchanged names and talked about the schools we attended, however, it was time to get back on the dance floor. This time, when the two of us met, during a set-dance, Rory (for that was his name) looked directly into my eyes. I wasn't sure whether or not I found him attractive, so I discreetly examined him, when his attention was elsewhere. He was quite tall and slim. His blackish hair fell, with a slight wave, over his dark, blue eyes. He would do, I decided, as I smiled, uncertainly, back at him. Suddenly, I was excited to be doing what I perceived to be a very adult activity. Having read several books where the hero and heroine had indulged in this sort of behaviour, I was fairly certain that what we had embarked on what was called flirting.

The evening seemed to fly by. In no time at all, it seemed, people were rushing off to the cloakroom to collect their coats. I saw my father walking towards me. I had forgotten all about him! Out of the corner of my eye, I also became aware of Rory, asking, "Can I walk you home?" Behind him, my father was nodding his assent, a wide grin spreading across his face. His unexpected consent confused me. Maybe I should go back with my friends, I wondered? After a cursory glance around, I realised that they had already drifted off. I had run out of options. My throat was getting drier, by the minute. Reluctantly, nodding to Rory, I found myself panicking, once more. Should I hold his hand? Should I let him put his arm around my shoulder? In my uncertainty, I placed my shiny bucket bag into my left hand, the hand he was trying to get hold of.

We progressed up the hill like this, with me swinging the bag, erratically, and edging away, any time I sensed that Rory wanted to touch me. He chatted, hesitantly, about some topic or other that I was unable to listen to, because of my preoccupation with keeping him from grabbing hold of me.

I came to a sudden stand-still when we arrived at my house. I didn't know what to do. Clumsily, I started to say goodnight to him. "Will you come to the pictures with me?" he asked, hurriedly. I realised he was asking me for a date! What should I say? "I'm not sure if I would be allowed to. I mean, I'm studying and everything. I'll have to find out from my parents," I managed to stutter back at him.

"Okay. Tell you what. Let's make a time, anyway. I'll see you here next Thursday, at around seven o'clock. That'll give you time to ask your parents. See you then." With that, he pushed his cold, moist, open, lips onto mine and was gone. I knocked on the door, relieved. The ordeal was over. I could breathe normally once more. Good Lord, I hadn't realised how difficult all this love stuff was. I would be glad to be curled up, safely, in my bed.

Over the next few days, I endured a certain amount of teasing from my sisters and parents. They managed to get the boy's name out of me but, no matter how I tried, I couldn't initiate a conversation about the dreaded date. Thursday was approaching and I hadn't asked if I could go to the cinema. I prayed that Rory would forget all about it, or would have changed his mind about wanting to take me but, no. On Thursday he arrived, expectantly, at the appointed time. My mother looked at me curiously, when I dashed to the door. "It's that boy. He wants to take me to the pictures," I stammered back at her. "What? On a school night? You never even mentioned it. You should have arranged it for the weekend!" my mother scolded me.

Opening the door and quickly blurting at him, "I'm not allowed to go. It's a school night." I carefully omitted to impart the rest of my mother's conversation, for suddenly I knew that I did not want to go out with him at all, not tonight, not at the weekend, not ever. This love-game was too much for me. It was wearing me out. It was causing me too much worry and distress. When I saw the look of disappointment on his face, I almost relented. I even walked down the street with him a short way, making feeble efforts to console him. I was tempted to arrange a time, during the following weekend, when we could meet.

Deep inside me, however, I was beginning to understand myself better. I wasn't ready for this grown-up carry-on. It was much more complicated than I had thought. Hastily throwing a "Cheerio," at him, I turned, abruptly, and ran home. My romantic development would have to take place between the covers of novels, for now. Real romance would have to wait. Still, I could claim to have had my first kiss, if anyone should ask. I was confident that I could embellish that memory from what I had already learned from fiction. No one would have to know that it had been an unexpected, hurried, clashing of inexpert lips and teeth.

A Song for Sally

What is she thinking? I'm sitting beside her, holding her swollen hands in mine, watching her eyes move slowly towards me. For twelve months she has been confined to this hospital bed. Gradually, she has been deteriorating, through a series of strokes, until at last, she has been left paralysed, able to communicate only by moving her eye lids, one blink for 'yes', two blinks for 'no'. Desperately, I try to imagine what that must feel like. Is she aware that she is lying here, imprisoned in a useless body? Can she see me? Does she recognize me?

I've been advised by my mother how to talk to her. "Just ask her questions with yes or no answers to them. She'll be able to answer you by blinking. 'Yes' is one blink. 'No' is two blinks. You'll soon get the idea." It's strange how inadequate the whole situation is making me feel. I am having difficulty gathering my thoughts. When I try to speak, I sound stilted. I seem to be speaking in a foreign language. I'm hesitant, suddenly inarticulate. Until now, I hadn't understood how important it was for me to hear the other side of a conversation. I need the stimulus of Sally's wry comments, her awkward, inquisitive questions, anything but this sad, hopeless silence.

I clear my throat noisily and murmur, nervously, "Aunt Sally, are you alright? I mean . . . I mean, are you comfortable?" The eyelids blink "Yes". At least, I hope it was a deliberate movement. I'm uncertain, now, if she blinked at all. Suddenly, I hear myself babbling. Instead of asking her dreary questions that require only "Yes" and "No" answers, I rush to tell her my news, what the flight coming over was like, how my children are probably managing without me. Even as I'm talking, my eyes are searching for a flicker, any sign that might convince me that there is a point to all of this. Does she have any real understanding of what I'm blabbing on about? But I have to keep going. I can't bear the emptiness, the echoing desolation. My mind drifts off to another time.

I am standing, terrified, at the top of a steep hill. Twenty minutes earlier, I had left home, with strict instructions from my mother to come down here to help my poor, crippled aunt. Of course I didn't see why I should have to waste my precious Saturday helping a stupid, old woman to clean her house or run errands for her, for that matter, even if she was my mother's older sister and my god-mother but, as usual, my mother had soon put me right about my duties. "You'll do it because I'm telling you to and that's all there is to it!" I knew it was pointless for me to argue but I made sure to throw her one of my famous, defiant looks, before stomping out of the house and running quickly down through our estate, past the familiar parade of shops and further down the uneven, concrete steps which led towards the street where my aunt lived.

There I stood, almost petrified, staring nervously down the sloping road, trying to figure out if I would be able to stop at all at Aunt Sally's door, for I was worried that my legs would be carried onward by the momentum of the almost sheer hill below. Tentatively, I edged my feet onto the pavement, taking care to stay close to the walls of the narrow, terraced houses, so that I would have something to hold on to, on the downward journey, should I need to In fact, I was worrying unnecessarily. Aunt Sally's house was towards the top of the street, so I was able to successfully navigate my way to her door, fairly quickly. Still, I didn't dare to look down, beyond her doorway, for fear I would be attacked by dizziness, so I glued my eyes to the all-important door knocker and, lifting my right hand, reluctantly, from the nearby wall. I thumped, urgently, on the door.

Suddenly she was there, in front of me, her right hand clutching a thick walking stick. She was not really as old as I had described her when quarrelling with my mother, but she was certainly worn-looking. Her flabby, middle-aged body was leaning forward, the weight hovering, lopsidedly, towards her stick. Her florid face seemed to be lurching down to meet mine. Two dark, beady eyes were searching my face, as if she was trying to peer right inside me. I stood absolutely still, afraid to breathe, willing myself not to cry. "You've come! It's great to see you! I knew you wouldn't let me down!" I felt myself being enveloped by the fleshy mound, her heavy walking-aid digging into my left shin. Within minutes, I was transferred from the hallway into the back kitchen, where a coal fire was burning and a table was set for four people. "I was just getting ready for the boys. They'll all be home soon."

What boys? Who was she talking about? Surely, she couldn't have boys, not at her age! I considered myself to have a certain amount of know-how in these matters; (after all, I was eleven years old!) but her remark mystified me. Sally threw me a shrewd look and smiled, to reassure me. "I suppose your mother forgot to mention. I keep boarders, just a couple of young fellas who used to live in the Children's Home up the road and then, of course, there's your Uncle Conor. He lives here with me, too." She was right that my mother had neglected to inform me about the 'home' boys, as those sorts of young men were known locally. I had forgotten all about Uncle Conor, myself.

He was an older brother of my mother's. In fact, at one time, all of us children had thought that Uncle Conor and Aunt Sally were a married couple but, as I grew older, I had learned that they were brother and sister. Aunt Sally's husband had deserted her years before but this matter was rarely spoken of in the family, being considered a shameful thing to have happened. All I knew for sure was that her husband lived in America, somewhere, and that their only daughter was now grown up, married with several children, and living on the same corporation estate where we lived.

Uncle Conor, by contrast, had never married. People talked about him as not being the full shilling, meaning that he was a bit slow. He had a ruddy, bony face, with a long nose and extremely prominent teeth. We children used to be fascinated to watch him eat an ice-cream wafer on his occasional Sunday visits to our house, for he chomped it quickly, with those large teeth, oblivious to how cold it was, while we delicately licked ours, allowing them to melt a little before we would bite into them. When he talked, he often stammered. He could become so agitated at the prospect of people listening to him. My mother had told us of his traumatic time at school, where he had been taunted by pupils and teachers alike for his inability to speak clearly. Although she was much younger than he was, she remembered her mother describing how she had angrily taken him away from school, at the age of seven, because of the cruel treatment that he had received while he was attending the local Christian Brothers' school and of how she, alone, had managed to prepare him for his First Communion, a fact of which she was extremely proud. Sadly, because he had had little formal schooling, he had never learned to read or write. Instead, my grandmother had trained him to run errands for her, and to perform various tasks for her around the house.

Sally had inherited Conor along with the family home, when my grandparents had died, since she had been living in their home for several years, along with her daughter, following her failed marriage. When I had the chance to observe their relationship closely, during my subsequent Saturday visits, the brother and sister seemed to behave more like a mother and son. Sally gave the orders and Conor carried them out, as well as he could, continuing in much the same way as he had done with his mother, carrying in buckets of coal and suchlike, or running errands for his sister. Although there were stormy scenes at times, when Sally would let fly at my uncle for some minor error he had made, she seemed genuinely protective of him, and he idolized her.

Already, on this first Saturday, my nostrils were being assailed by the strong smell of pigs' trotters, roasting in the oven. Over time, my Saturday excursions to Sally's would lead to me being introduced to other delicious aromas, such as spare ribs, roast lamb and the peculiar odour of boiling mutton, foodstuffs that were unofficially banned at home, because my father didn't like them, preferring beef products or, the occasional pork or lamb chop.

I soon became accustomed to Aunt Sally's somewhat brusque manner and, at times, fiery temper, which would be just as likely to evaporate into noisy laughter when something amusing caught her eye or her quick mind, or she had sized up how ludicrous a particular situation was. Her house always seemed to be bursting with grown ups. I was unused to this, being at the older end of a large family. There I would be, surrounded by the "home" boys, all several years older than me, Uncle Conor, sometimes my Uncle Jack, who used to drop by after putting a bet on the horses in the nearby bookies and frequently by Aunt Sally's drinking cronies, Maggy and Billie. It was in Sally's house that I was introduced to alcohol, not to taste it, of course, but I had never before witnessed whiskey and port being poured and drunk, since both of my parents were teetotal.

It wasn't too long before I had deduced why Sally was so keen to have me down to help her on Saturdays. I swiftly became her bookies' "runner". Regularly, throughout the day, I would be sent across the back lane to what looked like a large shed. There was a long, Formica counter running down one side of the interior. Behind the counter was a row of rectangular windows, free of glass, where several dingy-looking men, in checked caps, sat taking bets, handing over flimsy, yellow betting slips and paying out winnings to lucky punters. On my first visit to this alien, almost totally male environment, which I later learned was an illegal betting shop, I had difficulty being seen by any of them, on account of my short stature. Fairly quickly, however, they got used to my hands reaching up to them with money and a note that specified the horses' names, the race meetings and the kind of bet that Sally wanted to place. "Ah, sure, you're Sally's wee niece, aren't you," was a favourite comment when I had managed to struggle my way to a counter.

Back in her kitchen, we would frantically follow each race on the small, black and white television perched on top of the side-board. Sally cursed any horse that had the temerity to lose and, even worse, not to be placed. When she backed a winner, I could hear the excitement surge in her voice, as she calculated how much she had won. Each win was celebrated with a drink; each loss was commiserated over with an even larger one. If I was sent off with a winning betting slip, I could be sure of being handed back a half-crown, on my return, as my cut of the winnings.

Apart from my role as bookie's runner, Sally would often send me into the town to buy large bags of broken biscuits from Woolworth's, or huge cuts of silverside beef from the local butcher. These purchases would to be taken up to Sally's daughter, by me or more usually by Uncle Conor, who enjoyed walking anywhere around the town. He enjoyed meeting up with old acquaintances, who would often stop to enquire about Sally, who rarely left their home.

On one particular Saturday, near Christmas, Aunt Sally sent me to a local shoe shop, where she was well known, to pick up several pairs of house slippers of various sizes and styles. These were taken on approval or "appro", as she called it. Although I did not realise it at the time, this was her way of doing her Christmas shopping, ever since she had become housebound. She would order dozens of pairs of slippers with particular people in mind and then, depending on which of them arrived with a gift for her, she would make a present of slippers of a suitable size and style. Any that she did not give away would be returned to the shop.

Unfortunately for me, on this occasion, when I had heaved the bulky bags through Sally's doorway, one slipper was missing. No amount of matching up or counting could get away from the fact that, somehow, I had lost one of them. The remaining piece of footwear was flung at me, hitting me on the side of my forehead. Ignoring my sobs of protest, I was sent to retrace my steps, right back to the shop. It was to no avail. I returned without the precious match, only to have to endure more torrents of abuse. How could I be so stupid, so careless, *so* totally useless?

Did I expect her to give someone a single slipper as a gift? I had no opportunity to plead in my defence that the burden I had dragged from the shop was excessive and that Sally had no right to expect me to carry it, alone. She continued her rant until she eventually ran out of breath. I left for home, quivering with fear and indignation, vowing to myself that I would not be back, ever! Of course, the following Saturday, I was sent down by my mother to be greeted by a beaming Sally, who was able to inform me that the lost item had been picked up by a neighbour on her way home from shopping. The neighbour had talked about her find when she had attended a local wake that Uncle Jack had been to a few days after the incident, and he had been able to retrieve it for my aunt. There was not a word of apology for the upset she had put me through, or for the rage she had directed towards me. Sally celebrated the return of the prodigal slipper, almost as though she had won the pools.

Towards early evening, on most Saturdays, when I would be getting ready to return home and the company was becoming more affable, I might be called on to sing. "Come on, Kathleen, sing 'Scarlet Ribbons'. Sure, Maggy has never heard you," my aunt would solemnly assert, even though they had all probably heard it the previous week and several times before that. However, I would oblige, aware that I would be well-remunerated for my efforts.

On days when Sally's racing predictions had not gone well, there would be less money for me to jingle, climbing the rickety, stone steps towards home. On these occasions, she always managed to send me back home with some booty, even if it was a man's silver signet ring that she hunted out for me once, assuring me that it would be a perfect birthday present for my father – a man who never wore a bit of jewellery in his whole life. Another time, she produced a Jew's, or "Jaw's" harp, which I nearly broke my front teeth trying to play. My father, a musician, was quite impressed with that.

The wonder of my weekly visits to Sally's opened a vibrant world to me, the like of which I had not previously conceived. Its unpredictability excited me, although, at times I was frightened by dangerous, dark and aggressive emotions that could surface suddenly, but, just as quickly submerge. My aunt was someone who had to feel, physically, that she was alive. The mundane was not for her. There was a recklessness to her nature that drove all her actions, her gambling, her socialising, her drinking. Whether she was shouting with joy because her horse had won, or raising her voice in anger, because the fire hadn't been set properly, she sparkled with life.

Now, looking down on the pathetic, prone figure, the eyes staring helplessly up at me, an outrageous idea occurred to me. Catching my breath, I thought, defiantly: "Why not?" It would be no worse than trying to converse with her in this pitiful manner. I glanced around the ward. It was a quiet part of the day and most of the other patients were dozing, peacefully. Keeping my hands in Sally's, I began, hesitantly, and then more confidently, to sing: "I peeped in to say good-night and then I heard my child in prayer......."

The expression in her eyes seemed to soften. A single teardrop rolled down Sally's left cheek. Her fingers tightened round mine, as the song reverberated around the hospital ward.

(This story was written for the Writers' Group based in Arnold's Hotel, and first published in the magazine, *Ireland's Own*.)

Christmas Past

When I consider my childhood Christmases, it is difficult to separate out in my memory which incident happened in any particular year. There was the year when I took my present to church with me. A new black and white striped bag, filled with sweets from my stocking, so that I would have something to sustain me after I had taken Communion. Was that the same year that I posed around the house in my nurse's uniform? I tested the reflexes of various brothers and sisters with the plastic hammer from my doctor's bag, that also contained within it a real working thermometer (or so I thought, anyway) and a grey and pink stethoscope, for me to check that everyone's heart was beating regularly. Maybe it was on that same Christmas that I fought with my sister Kay, over identical baby dolls. We had each claimed the same doll and had pulled on it so violently that we managed to yank its leg off. I remember that my father's swift response to our actions was to grab both dolls from us and leave us to grieve over their loss until, several days after the celebration, they were quietly returned to us.

Maybe the Christmas morning we children discovered a huge cardboard box under the tree, labelled *From Santa. Not to be opened till after dinner* was the same day that Kay and I had our fight. Or was that the time that my godmother sent up a huge, boxed, china doll, with eyelashes that could really blink, and blonde hair, arranged in ringlets? To my disappointment some days after, when I had vigorously brushed out the curls, her hair was left matted and uneven. I don't remember playing with her much, after that.

To get back to that box, left for us under the tree. Of course, we were all intrigued by it. In fact, we endeavoured to eat our festive dinner quickly, we were so curious to find out what its contents were. When it was eventually unsealed, later that afternoon, it was brim full with little toys, each one wrapped in colourful paper. Our parents organised us, in turn, to dip our hands in and pull out a surprise, which each child then had to unwrap, to squeals of delight from the others. My favourite surprise was a monkey-on-a-stick, which I pushed up and down for the rest of the evening and for many days after. I learned, much later, when I was grown up, that our parents had been inspired to fill the box up the night before, when they were sorting out our stockings and realised that they had bought too many toys and games for us all that year. My mother was in the habit of buying stocking fillers every time she went out shopping, for months before the great event. That year, she had been over-enthusiastic and had come up with the 'lucky dip' idea, late on Christmas Eve, when she was becoming too tired to sort out the smaller items. She was anxious to get to bed, for, at least, a couple of hours before we would be running into the bedroom, to show my father and her what "Santa" had brought us.

The first Christmas that we were able to watch television, I remember seeing the set being carried, carefully, into the living room by my father and placed on a tall table, between the fireplace and the window. It was black and white, with a fourteen-inch screen and had been rented for the holiday. There was only one station, the BBC, but we were satisfied to gaze at the test card even, it was such a wonder to us.

Sorting out the chronology of what happened is further complicated by the memories of events that happened every single year, during our traditional family Christmas. There are many common themes and customs relating to this most important festival. Yet different families and cultures tend to interpret them in their own ways. For me, as a child, Christmas meant the excitement of writing a letter to Santa, weeks before. This activity was followed by frantic, sooty, attempts to send my letter up the chimney, for Santa's bird to catch and deliver to the great man.

There was the added difficulty of trying to maintain an unblemished record of good behaviour during the month of December, at least, because every fool knew it was that self-same bird which listened on his perch by the chimney for signs of naughty children who, of course, would not receive presents, no matter how many letters they might send upwards.

The greatest anticipation, however, was reserved for Christmas Eve night, when we children, already bathed early and wrapped warmly in fresh pyjamas, would be seated beside my Aunt Katy. We were obviously peering out of the front window of our house towards the distant Donegal hills, to keep watch for Santa's reindeer and sleigh, as he glided over the darkening sky. It was considered a great honour to be the person who first caught sight of the traveller, so we all eagerly searched the horizon, ready to shout triumphantly that we could see him. That sighting was always our cue to go to bed, but not before we had ensured that a candle was lit at the window, to welcome all travellers to our home on such an auspicious night. A glass of sherry, accompanied by a large slice of fruit cake, was set on the kitchen table, for Santa to enjoy, when he had clambered down the chimney.

Every Christmas morning, after we had each dragged our filled stockings (usually pillowcases) up from the bottom of our beds and ransacked them, amidst loud whoops of delight and surprise, we would descend on our parents' room with some of the booty and let them know what we had received. After hearing my mother's faint expressions of astonishment and my father's muffled grunts such as; did we realize it was not even six o'clock, all the children who had made their First Communion would get dressed in our best clothes and hurry up the hill to early Mass, where we would meet friends and exchange information about what presents we had been given.

Coming back home, afterwards, we would be met by the delicious whiff of turkey and, especially, the strong-smelling soup which would have been simmering all morning in an enormous, black pot, sent up the previous evening from my aunt's. It would have been lifted onto the cooker, turkey carcass and all, by my father, before he had retired to bed.

Breakfast was always an insignificant affair, as we would have already opened our selection boxes after Mass and would be looking forward to a sumptuous dinner of turkey soup, followed by a main course of roast potatoes, parsnips, carrots, peas, stuffing and the all-important turkey meat itself, accompanied by thick, tasty gravy. In our house, the serving of the dinner was a ritual. Because we were such a large family (eventually, there were thirteen children) Christmas Day was one of the few occasions when we sat down for a meal together.

The table would be lifted from the kitchen into the living room. Every seat in the house would be utilized, including bedroom chairs and the piano stool. There would be a tablecloth decorated with designs of holly and bells or some such, with napkins, crackers and glasses at each place. We children would be instructed to sit down, while our parents dished up the soup, my mother filling the bowls from the black pot and my father darting rapidly from kitchen to living room, serving each of us. At these times, they might become overwrought, perhaps, if one of us dared to complain that he wanted his soup strained, because he or disliked vegetables, or the strong, turkey flavour.

The second course would be served only when everyone had finished the soup, by my father alone, who would ask each of us what we wanted on the plate, especially what sort of meat we wanted, dark or light-coloured. He would reserve the legs for himself and my older brother, Bernard. In between courses, we would pull our crackers and put on our party hats, which had to be worn through-out the meal and even, sometimes, until bed-time by some of the more enthusiastic members of the family. Homemade Christmas pudding would only be offered to those who had some appetite left. Most of us kept that delight for another day, as we had generally over-indulged by then.

During the rest of the afternoon and evening, we children would play with toys, or read, or fill in colouring books, while our exhausted parents would doze off. We also listened to carols on the radio, or, when we had acquired a television, watching Christmas entertainment. In those days, most people stayed at home for all of Christmas Day. I don't remember being forbidden to leave the house. There was just an understanding that we should stay indoors, so it would be the next day before we could show off our presents to our friends.

On St Stephen's Day, a group of us would visit the cribs of the Holy Family, displayed in the various churches in the town, so, by the time we would return, wearily, from these lengthy pilgrimages, the urgency of boasting about what Santa had brought us might have receded. The holiday stretched in front of us for a week or so but the magic of Christmas would have to wait for another whole year!

Confidant

I talk to my father on most days, usually when I'm in bed, late at night, unable to sleep because of some nagging worry or other. By being able to confide in him like this, I can then relax enough to sleep. It is peculiar that I use my father in this way because I don't remember having any intimate conversations with him, when he was alive. He was, indeed, a man of few words. In our home, my mother was the communicator, who busily organized all of us, including my father. Occasionally, when the turmoil of family life became too much for her, she was the parent who scolded and shouted at us for neglecting to carry out chores to her exacting standards.

In contrast, our father only had to raise his brow and glare directly at the offender to signal that he was upset and had been pushed beyond his tolerance limit. Those occasional displays of temper from him had much more effect on our behaviour than my mother's frequent chidings. My father had great difficulty in expressing his feelings, either physically or verbally. My first real memory of kissing him was on my wedding day, when I hugged him tightly to me and managed to plant a passionate, tipsy, kiss on his lips. In some ways, though, he was what people nowadays would describe as a 'new' man. He regularly cooked dinner and got us children ready for bed, usually checking we had brushed our teeth properly, or had thoroughly scrubbed the backs of our necks. I have an abiding memory of him, holding my chin in a vice-like grip, while scrubbing my face with a face flannel, simultaneously singing, "Hello, Patsy Fegan…." Whenever I hear that song, I am transported back, in an instant. I feel my skin tingling from the towel that he used to rub my face dry.

Although he was an excellent musician and singer, my father never really encouraged any of his offspring to perform. When he was a child, he had been forced to compete in Feis competitions by his ambitious mother and older sisters. Consequently, he had an aversion to pushy parents and to competitions, in general. It was my mother who sent us to singing lessons and who eagerly entered us for the annual Derry Feis. My father's reluctant contribution would be to hear each of us perform our set piece, the night before the event.

I'm convinced that my father's premature death, aged sixty-three, from a heart attack, was a direct result of his inability to express his feelings, especially, his paternal love. My brother had been killed, seven years before, aged twenty-one. My father was unable to deal with the obscene reality that he had failed to protect his irreverent, cheeky, youngest son. After Dennis's death, he tried hard to improve communication with his surviving children. Often he would instigate self-conscious conversations which would, inevitably, peter out, to our mutual relief. He was painfully unable to utter, "I'll miss you," or "I love you," paralysed by his terrible shyness. My father dealt with his son's bereavement by collecting as many photographs of him as he could and by making a memoriam album of him. Unlike my mother, who was able to express her grief verbally and actively, my father, imprisoned by his deeply repressed emotions, only managed occasional, uncharacteristic, outbursts of anger. To his family, who had rarely before heard him discussing any topic at length, these inarticulate rages were terrifying and painful to witness.

Yet, there is a side to my father that I remember as exhilarated and extrovert. This was the father who would confidently pick up his violin or guitar and lead family parties, performing in his own, inimitable style, smiling widely at us, encouraging us to sing out, in the choruses. At these times, we knew that he was totally in charge, able to lighten or darken our moods, depending on the music he chose to play. Even today, when we have family gatherings, at a certain part of the evening we sing as many of my father's songs as we can remember. It brings us all close to him, once more.

I guessed my singing had almost come up to his high standards the night he invited me to sing a song at a "seisun" he was running, in a local pub. It was the final time I was ever to be out with him, socially, on my last visit home before he died. For many years, I had yearned for him to show me some indication that he thought I had inherited even a little of his musical talent. By asking me to sing in front of his fellow musicians and fans, I knew that he was signalling his approval. I glowed in the shimmering light of his recognition.

The last time I heard his voice was during a telephone conversation, when he was advising me to end my unhappy marriage. Knowing that, as a fervent Catholic he had great difficulty with the whole concept of divorce, I could only listen in silent admiration to his sympathetic tones and marvel at his ability, this time, to speak all the right words. It is this tolerant, caring and, at last, articulate father that I talk to, late into the night, for I know, in his wisdom, he will always be able to help me to decide what it is I need to do.

A Bitter Departure

"Why?" The woman walks along the riverbank, the stark question echoing inside her head, until the pain becomes almost unbearable. Why had he done it? As she walks, her eyes frantically scrutinize the choppy, dirt-grey waters, searching desperately for some sign of her beautiful, precious son. He was here, somewhere. She had known that from the moment she had read that dreadful letter she had found propped up on the kitchen table, ten long days ago. She had not wanted to believe her own flesh and blood could plan such an awful ending – to jump off a bridge, to kill himself and not even to give any explanation. That was the worst part somehow, to not know his reason for doing it. The question has haunted her ever since.

Every day she has come here, desperate to be close to him, even in death, convinced, somehow, that by being here she will be able to make sense of his decision. Her husband and other children are spending their days treading these same paths, peering hopelessly, like her, into the river near to where Brian had been spotted, in the early morning mist, climbing quite deliberately over the wrought-iron rails of the familiar local landmark. Apparently, he had carefully steadied his lanky six foot frame, before plunging into the murky, ice-cold currents.

She feels as though she has died herself, and that she has moved on to some agonizing purgatory, damned to wander along the river's edge, forever waiting for his battered, bloated body to shoot up to the surface. Friends and relatives have tried to stop her coming to this place. They are worried that she will be present when his body is discovered. They know the corpse will be in a dreadful state, but they don't understand her needs. She does not care what he will look like. She has already rehearsed in her mind the worst possible scenario, yet she feels compelled to witness his watery home-coming, to wrap her arms around his wet chest, to hug him to her, for one last time. She is his mother, for God's sake. She gave him life. Nothing else matters.

At night, she sleeps sporadically, willing the darkness to end so she can go out once more into the wintry landscape to resume her desolate search. She barely tastes the food that kind neighbours place in front of her. They fail to realize how guilty she feels, eating when he can no longer do so. She is betraying her child by continuing to go through the motions of living, when he has not even been laid to rest.

Brian had been her first-born, the oldest of her four children. There had been a special bond between them, from his first moment of life, for he had been born prematurely, before she had even made it to the hospital. She remembers being alone in that bedroom, while her sister was downstairs frantically phoning the emergency services. Her screams of pain and fear had not subsided until her son had pushed his determined way out, a tiny, shrivelled and silent infant. The doctors had not expected him to survive because he had arrived so early. Doggedly, however, he had proved them wrong. She remembered her joy when she was, at last, allowed to bring him home, all five pounds of him. She had grown so used to his small size, by then, that she had found it amusing when others were reluctant to hold him. They had been frightened of damaging his fragile frame.

As he grew older, that earlier bond between them grew stronger. She had been proud to be his chief confidant. He shared with her worries about such things as his schoolwork, or minor squabbles he had with friends. Later, when he had been concerned about his father's reactions to him being dropped from the school football team, or when he had wanted to form a rock band, she had been there to reassure him and protect him. It was when he reached puberty, to her later regret, that she had been forced to curb his general frankness. She had been embarrassed by his attempts at that time to confide in her the details of his first, faltering sexual experiences. She had explained to him that it was not seemly to discuss such matters with one's mother. There were some things a parent was better not to know about her child. Gradually, he had stopped talking to her about such intimate subjects and, although she was relieved not to have to listen to his explicit descriptions, she felt vaguely disappointed that their close relationship had weakened somehow.

Each heavy step she now takes accuses her of letting him down. Why hadn't she allowed him to continue to share his worries? She had pushed him away when he needed her. Maybe she could have prevented this tragedy. Yet he had seemed happy, that was the problem. There had been no hint of difficulties, at all. Each time she had been with him in the past months, he had appeared content and relaxed. He had laughed and made jokes all through the recent Christmas celebrations. He had participated, enthusiastically, in all of the family festivities, entertaining them at the dinner table with amusing anecdotes about some of his pupils. He had seemed to be successful and contented in his teaching career, at last.

There had been a time, the mother admitted to herself now, when she had been concerned about him. He had seemed so depressed, convinced that he had chosen the wrong profession. That had been a few years ago, when he had confessed to her his difficulties with classroom control. He was afraid he might end up hurting one of the pupils if he lost his temper some day, he told her. She had convinced him to persevere. She was sure every teacher had doubts like that. Now, she wondered. Should she have intervened? Maybe she should have encouraged him to leave, instead, to find something else to do, something that would not cause him so much distress?

I'm sorry. I can't see any other way out. I've decided what I must do. By the time you read this letter, it will all be over for me. When I leave here, I'm going to walk to the old bridge. The river is deep there and the currents are fast. There should be no possibility of me failing. I just need to end my agony. Please try to forgive me. I love you all. Love, Brian.

These parting words have been replaying over and over in her mind. She could recite the entire script. She has examined them, tried to find clues in them that might explain what he has done. Part of her even tries to fantasize that he has not killed himself at all. Maybe he is safe somewhere else. He has just run away and is too scared to come back. He is unable to face everyone's ridicule. She knows that these desperate aspirations are not true. She has already spoken to witnesses who watched him jump from the railing but, for short periods, she makes herself believe that he is still alive. She maintains her sanity with wild imaginings, when the intensity of her grief becomes too much to bear.

Before he decided to take up teaching, Brian had been sure his hip-hop band was going to be a huge success. They had started playing together when they were very young and had quickly become popular in clubs, and around the university circuit. They were praised in music magazines for their youthful talent. Various well-known people in the business had wanted to promote them, but the boys had been afraid of exploitation. They had read so many horror stories of how different music heroes of theirs had been treated when they were fresh and naïve. They hadn't wanted the same thing to happen to them, so they had been overly-cautious. Somehow, their opportunities had dissipated. As they hesitated, other young bands took over. Suddenly, they found that fewer managers were interested in them. The disappointment had been difficult to cope with. It had all seemed such a waste.

Brian had been luckier than the other band members, however. As well as playing music, he had always continued his academic studies and had achieved an excellent degree in mathematics. She had laughed when he told her he had done that for her, to make her proud. The silly boy, he had no need to impress her, she assured him. Wasn't she already proud of him? Still, she was glad he had a back-up plan, especially when it became obvious that the band's dreams of fame and fortune had come to nothing.

Was that the reason? Had he hidden his devastation from her? Had he, in fact, been unable to come to terms with that disappointment? An overwhelming sense of desolation hits her abruptly, causing her to catch her breath. Her throat closes over, choking her. Slowly, she forces air into her lungs and then out again, trying to regain a steady rhythm. That was something else her poor, dead son would never do again. Tears that rarely stop flowing these days drip relentlessly down the tip of her nose and into her parched mouth. Would there ever be any ease from this terrible, physical torture? The nightmare is dragging her in, squeezing out all of her desire to continue living. Will finding his body help her? She does not know. The need to reclaim him is so strong, but will it make any difference?

Rosa had approved of Maire, a junior doctor her son had met last year. Truth to tell, she had been relieved when she learned that Brian had a steady girlfriend. She had always wondered, when his many romances broke up after very short periods, that maybe . . . she was reluctant even to think, never mind to voice her suspicions that her darling son might be homosexual, not that she was prejudiced, of course she wasn't. Rosa had always insisted that she had very liberal views about those sorts of things. Still, when it was your oldest son you were considering, well, that was different, wasn't it?

Just a few weeks ago, Brian had hinted that Maire was thinking of moving in with him. The mother had eagerly told her son how pleased she would be if they wanted to live together. However, when the girl had returned to her parents' house before Christmas without any final arrangements being made, Rosa had worried that the couple had changed their minds. Had they fought about something? Were they breaking up? But surely the girl had been as numbed as they were when she learned of Brian's disappearance. She had returned to their town as soon as she heard. She could think of no explanation, she told them. Rosa was too preoccupied with her search to notice Maire's uncharacteristic taciturnity during those first dreadful days.

The expected telephone call came through to the house a week later, as Rosa and her husband were about to set off for another futile day of searching. A canoeist had spotted what appeared to be a man's body, caught under some weeds. Divers had been sent to investigate. They were already in the water, trying to free the obstacle. The caller advised Jack, her husband, to come down to the riverside, in case he would be needed for identification. Rosa insisted on accompanying him. With resignation, he led her to the car. Secretly, he was grateful that he would not have to face the ordeal alone. What if it wasn't even their son? Would they be able to continue this limbo existence?

Three days later they were able to hold the funeral. His parents had recognized him, alright, even with the gruesome changes he had undergone. It would do them no good to dwell on the bites and bruises covering his dear, swollen face, or to examine too closely the soft torn tissue on all of his limbs. The couple had collapsed into each other's arms when they had nodded their affirmation to the waiting pathologist. They were not allowed to touch him, but Rosa realized immediately that she did not want to hold him, after all. He was gone. She could accept that now. Any remaining tendrils of hope had melted away when she stared at the distorted, bloated cadaver lying on the cold, plastic sheet.

At the graveside, the diminished family clung together, sobbing sorely. Someone quietly mentioned 'closure', that maybe they would be able to resume their lives, now that they had somewhere to visit, a place where they could come to talk to Brian.

Maire, standing with the family, knew now was not the time to share with the parents her own suspicions. Now his body had been found, she knew they deserved to know what he had confided to her the last time she had been with him. She could not yet bear to tell them of their son's doubts, his tearful apologies to her. He had struggled so hard and so long to fight his natural urges, she knew that. He had been forced to face up to them only when he had felt compelled to release her from her rash promise to marry him. He would never be any use to her as a husband. His desires and preferences were elsewhere, he had wearily confessed to her. They were not directed towards her or towards any woman, he had sobbed. The young woman glanced over at Rosa. She would never rest until she knew why her handsome, clever, son had destroyed himself, that much was obvious. She would have to be told, sometime but not yet. Maire's exhausted brain reverberated with the relentless question, "When? When will the time be right?"

Separation

Aine O'Donnell was raised in the North of Ireland, during the 1930s, while Gregory, her father, lived far away in America. When Selina, her darling mother, had become pregnant with Aine, in New Jersey, the young couple were already experiencing marital difficulties. What had seemed to be an exhilarating adventure for the two of them, whenever they had been planning their new life back home in Ireland, had deteriorated into a mundane, tedious existence, soon after they had arrived in the America of the late Twenties.

Almost right away, Selina had been disappointed to discover that the glamorous world she had learned of in Hollywood films and movie magazines was a very different place from the dull suburbs they inhabited. Her new husband worked long shifts at a local automobile factory. Her days were spent in the company of other, older, Irish immigrant wives, each of them with two or three children to keep them busy. These women were always keen to contrast their relative affluence, in this great United States of America, with the bleak, poverty-stricken lives many of their families were enduring back home. She wondered, "Where were the beautiful, fabulously furnished apartments she had expected? Where were the Musical Theatres, the night-clubs, the overly abundant shopping arcades?" She craved for the bright lights of her aspirations.

The husband, who had idolised her for several years before he had even managed to gather up enough courage to ask for her hand in marriage, conversely – in this strange country – found himself suddenly disillusioned by his brash young wife. He compared her, unfavourably, with some of the American women that he worked with. They had an air of sophistication about them, he thought. Even at work, they dressed smartly, attractively. They knew how to talk to a man, how to treat him with respect. They were forever complimenting him and praising him for being such a willing, tireless, worker.

Selina, by contrast, often walked around in her nightclothes for most of the day, even when his male friends were around. She was very outspoken about the dreary life she considered they were living. She wanted the excitement of the city of New York that she had dreamt of, when they were back in Derry. He was unable to deter her from talking of her disappointed dreams aloud, in company. Gregory was embarrassed by her noisy dissatisfaction. It gave him strong feelings of inadequacy.

There was also the problem of her limp. Back home, he had been so dazzled by her strong, vivacious, personality that her peculiar gait, caused, he knew, by childhood polio, had merely enhanced her charm. In this new country, with a fresh circle of acquaintances, he was ashamed of her appearance. People over here regarded her as a cripple, a drain, financially, to the country. Although he knew she had been a hard worker back in Ireland, he allowed his new friends' comments to feed his growing resentment of her. He was the one who had to rise early each day while she stayed in bed, sometimes until near mid-day, he had been told by well-meaning neighbours.

He felt guilty about these thoughts when he found out that she was expecting a baby, a few months after their arrival. Nevertheless, he was relieved when she suggested returning to Ireland for the birth of the child. It would be easier for her, she told him. Her mother and sisters would be there to help. She missed having them around her. Gregory was relieved to be released, at least temporarily, from the responsibility of taking care of his burdensome wife and, soon, a child. "I'll write every week," he assured her. "When the baby is old enough to travel, I'll send you the return tickets."

Their daughter, Aine, was born some months after Selina had endured a terrible, three-week sea voyage, during which time she had been violently ill, from a combination of sea sickness and the pregnancy. Mother and child then had to share a small, cramped family home with her parents and Selina's younger siblings. The young mother could not contemplate the return sea journey yet. As several months passed, letters and parcels arrived, intermittently, from Gregory but there was no longer any mention of a definite date for their return. After the terrible Wall Street Crash, which had occurred soon after Aine's birth, life had become increasingly difficult for working people like Gregory. Like millions of others, his hours at the factory had been cut. Eventually, he became yet another unemployment statistic, as his firm, too, went into liquidation. He found himself competing even for the most menial, short-term work with other immigrant workers, many younger and even more desperate than he was.

His wife felt abandoned, by the time Aine had celebrated her first birthday in her grandparents' home. Selina's father had not approved of his daughter's return to Ireland. He considered that she should have stayed by her young husband's side. Deep down, he also regretted his role in encouraging her to marry Gregory O'Donnell. He had always felt that they were unsuited. The young man was too much of a day-dreamer for his forceful and bossy daughter, yet Mr Donaghey had allowed himself to be persuaded by his wife that marriage would be good for both of the young people. They would balance each other out, she had assured him. Now, in his own home, his guilt caused the father to ignore Selina, as much as he could, given her large presence, although he surreptitiously doted on his little grand-daughter, Aine.

He was already grieving the absence of his oldest son, Patrick, who had left home a few months before Selina's return, following a terrible row. The older man had been fiercely against his son joining the British Army. "No son of mine will wear that uniform!" he had roared to his favourite son, when he learned of his intentions. Patrick tried, in vain, to point out to him that it was his only chance of a career or regular work, coming from this town of high unemployment. However, Mr. Donaghey was deeply embittered by the death, during the Great War, of his younger brother, John, who had naively taken the King's Shilling, amid promises that he would be helping to free Ireland, after the war. He could not bear to sacrifice another loved one to a country that had reneged, so completely, on its promise. The English were not to be trusted, ever. "If you leave this house to join up, you'll not come back to it!" he had shouted, passionately. "I'll disown you!" When Patrick obstinately continued with his plans, his father had been heartbroken. He forbade the whole family from speaking Patrick's name, ever, in his presence.

The years passed with no resolution to the long separation. Selina worked sporadically, in local shirt factories, mostly staying in her parents' home. Occasionally, when tempers within the over-crowded household became too frayed, she shifted, with her daughter, to the house of one or other of her married sisters. Communication between herself and her husband had diminished to a couple of letters a year, although she was quietly alert to the possibility that one day the elusive travel documents might arrive, especially as businesses in America began to stabilise and to flourish, once more.

Meantime, Aine grew older, almost as a sister to her younger aunt and uncles. From time to time, she enjoyed the excitement of receiving parcels from her absent father, whom she knew only from one faded, curling, wedding photograph. She dreamt, frequently, of travelling to America on a great ship to meet him. Sometimes she imagined herself answering the front door to a loud knock, to find her own, dear father standing on the doorstep. She desperately craved for his physical presence. She was envious of friends who had fathers at home. She loved to hear them talk even about disagreements they were having with them. Of course, she couldn't conceive ever falling out with the father that she had invented for herself. He would always be handsome, kind and easy for her to confide in, she was confident of that.

The outbreak of the Second World War put a stop to the, by now, infrequent gifts from America. Aine was maturing. She was becoming aware of some of the advantages of having an absent father. It made it easier for her to prevail on her harassed mother to allow her to wear high-heels and make-up, long before her friends were able to. Although her grandfather strongly disapproved of her teetering about, covered in "war-paint", as he called her inexpertly-applied make-up, he had no control in these matters. Indeed, her mother seemed to delight in defying him and in indulging her only child's whims.

The war also brought many sailors to the port where they lived. By the early Forties, many thousands of American sailors stopped off there for re-fuelling. She fantasised, constantly, that her father would be one of them. One of Gregory's sisters, Aunt Peggy, who lived nearby, had told them he was in the American Navy but, because he had ceased to write to them, by then mother and daughter had no idea where he had been posted. Aine's desperate need to meet this man had not really lessened. She worried. Why had he never come to rescue her and bring her to America, her proper home? Maybe he did not think her pretty enough, from the many photographs that had been sent out to him. Maybe he had resented her being born a girl. She wanted to write to him, to ask him these questions that were consuming her but she was afraid of his answers. She preferred the uncertainty of not knowing. That way, she could hold on to her dreams.

Selina and Aine no longer mentioned Gregory's name in each other's presence. There had been no real agreement about this. It was just that the vision they used to share, in Aine's early childhood, of returning triumphantly together to America, had gradually faded for both of them, as they each faced the bitter reality of everyday life and the disappointment of lost hopes and ambitions. Aine dared not risk hurting her mother by using Gregory's name. She realised that Selina still loved him and felt badly treated by him and, now, the turmoil of war seemed to have curtailed any hope of a re-uniting.

Occasionally, when Aine visited her Aunt Peggy, she would hear scraps of what he was doing, though she was not given an address to write to any more. Sometimes, Peggy would imply that her father was too ashamed to resume contact. He had neglected her for so long that it was probably too late. He had missed his chance. Aine was confused how to answer these comments. She was young and inarticulate. She longed to say, straight out, "Give me his address. I'll write to him and tell him it's alright," but she remained silent, terrified of rejection. Aine's daydreams about her father became more romantic and less realistic. She knew that he needed to fight, to help rid the world of Hitler's Nazi Army. She was confident that he would perform his duties heroically. Alone, however, she had a longing to see him, to touch him, to hold him close to her.

When the war eventually came to an end, her anxiety to meet him seemed to fade. Now a young woman, she became involved in the serious business of meeting boys. She shared with her mother a strong zest for life, for socialising and for living in the moment. Like Selina, she could rise, phoenix-like, from the ashes of broken dreams, ready to move on to her next venture. Her enthusiasm endeared her to everyone. Tears never lasted with her. Optimism shone out in her infectious smile. Her popularity with boys was well-established because of her talent for dancing. She was rushed at every dance she went to. She attended local dance halls with friends, flirting with eager dancing partners.

Eventually, she met the man who was to become her husband, a singer for one of the dance bands. When he saw her dancing, he immediately became enthralled by her. He watched her at social functions, for several weeks, before he approached her. Although he was some years older than her, it was not long before they fell deeply in love.

Her mother was concerned that her precious daughter was growing up too quickly. Surely, she was too young to marry? Selina's own experience had made her cynical of all men's sincerity. She could not bear to have this child suffer, as she had. She did not want her to be made a figure of ridicule and pity, yet she was wise enough not to interfere. She knew her daughter was as head-strong as she was.

Reluctantly, she accepted an early wedding date. She thought bitterly of what her husband would think about his child, whom he had not ever seen, getting married. She pondered on the role he should be playing, walking Aine up the aisle, handing her over to her new bridegroom. She considered writing to him, to inform him of the marriage, but her pride could not bear another snub from him. It was five years from his last letter to her. Subsequent correspondence from her had been ignored. She consoled herself that maybe he had moved, leaving no forwarding address. Pride forbade her from questioning members of his family about his whereabouts. Anyway, he had long ago given up contacting them. Presumably, he had made a new life for himself. She was unable to face learning the details of what this new life was.

Aine seemed consumed by her wedding preparations. She organized a local dressmaker to copy a dress she had spotted in a woman's magazine. It had been difficult, although, luckily, not impossible to purchase the material she wanted, for even though the war had been over for several years, fabric was still scarce. She drew up a large guest list, making sure to include her father's side of the family. She was unsure whether any of them would turn up, except Aunt Peggy, who had been the only one of them to keep in contact with her over the years. Indeed, the woman had always tried to compensate for her father's abandonment by making a special fuss of her at birthdays and Christmas times. Because she wanted to ensure her aunt was kept appraised of all the arrangements, she would slip down to her house, at times when her mother was visiting friends.

On the morning of the wedding, the house was crammed with different people; some relatives helping the bride to get dressed, others helping her mother get everything ready for the wedding breakfast that was being laid out in the largest upstairs bedroom. Her grandmother was hurrying after her grandfather, scolding him for not staying still long enough to have his dress-tie fixed, properly. Because he would be giving Aine away, he was particularly nervous and short-tempered. Some of her female cousins were trying to calm him down, without success. He stomped irritably around the house, avoiding his, by now, distracted wife and getting in the way of various preparations.

Amidst the cacophony, someone knocked loudly on the front door. Aine's young Uncle Liam, who was standing nearby, opened it, assuming it to be the driver of the car that was to take the bride and her entourage to the church. A tall, balding, rather overweight man, dressed in a smart navy suit, stood outside, a hesitant smile forming on his face. Liam staring, assured him, "They're not quite ready. They'll be down in a wee minute." The stranger continued smiling at him, though by now a strained look hovered around in his eyes. "Do you not know me, Liam? Sure I recognise you, even if you have gone and got all grown up on me!"

The loud, half-familiar tones caused Liam to examine him more closely. There was something in that voice that he recognised, yet there was something strange, too, an odd twang in the accent. The man continued, stammering a little. "I . . . I've come to . . ." Behind them, the household was suddenly silent, every movement and sound frozen, except for the rustle of Aine's dress, as she pushed her way to the front door. Her face was intensely pale, her eyes fixed on the stranger's face. "Daddy? Daddy! I knew you would come, I prayed you would make it, once you knew, once Aunt Peggy . . ." Her voice faded, as she slumped forward, to be caught, clumsily, by the awkward stranger. It was her Uncle Patrick, whom until that moment, she had never met.

BRIDIE TIMMONS

The Playboy

It was a perfect autumn afternoon, with nature seeming reluctant to go to sleep, and there was a feeling of excitement and joy about the town. William felt alive and excited as he walked along, although he didn't quite know why he felt this way. Perhaps it was the smiling faces of the shoppers. William imported and sold household goods, though there was nothing of great value. They were just basic paper goods, small gadgets, rugs, china, and bric-a-brac. They were all a little more upmarket than a pound shop, but very lucrative, nonetheless . . .

William was a strong character. He worked hard and played hard. He was divorced, and in his late Forties, and he belonged to all the right local organisations. He went to the gym three times a week, and he played on the local 'oldies' football team. William was fit and healthy, and a well-known local figure. Women liked him, and he was seeing two women at the same time, though neither of them knew. Julie was about thirty, or so she said, but William often wondered about that. She worked in a local hotel as receptionist-cum-barmaid, and she was very pretty, good fun and sexy. Even thinking of her reminded William how much he liked her, but did he *love* her? He didn't think so, but would he really recognise such a thing as love, after all these years on his own, after his failed marriage?

Lying in bed last night Julie had turned her attractive body towards him and staring pointedly at him, she had asked bluntly: "Would you ever think of marrying me William?" He had been stunned and shocked, at her directness. Marry her? The thought had never crossed his mind, but he began to think about it. After all she would be a great partner. She was good fun, she was sexy, and a hard worker. That was an attractive combination of qualities, but somehow she did not bring out the softer caring side of him that he remembered feeling towards his ex-wife.

However, William was also seeing Alice. He had met her at a local hotel a few months earlier. He had an eye for a pretty woman, and he had noticed her during the meeting, so at the tea-break he made sure he introduced himself. Alice was older than William, and also divorced, but with grown-up children. She was most attractive, and William found himself telling her things that he would normally not talk about.

She was clever. But also vulnerable, and she brought out his gentler side. Soon they became lovers, and he was shocked to discover that a woman older than him could be so attractive. He had tried to stop seeing her but had really missed her when he tried to break it off. He found her quite shy in bed, and when he mentioned this, she replied with a quiet little laugh, "I'm out of practice!" One of her greatest attractions was that somehow she made him feel in charge. William, however, was used to being with different women, and he made a point of not telling Alice about Julie.

As William continued his walk, and thought about his women, suddenly the sun went in and he shivered. The afternoon became darker and much colder and William's good mood changed. He suddenly felt tired, and out of sorts, and began to look forward to getting home and relaxing.

Later on that evening, as he watched television, William found it impossible to settle himself. He paced around the garden, but still this feeling of gloom and restlessness persisted. He decided to ring Julie, but her careless cheerfulness only irritated him, and he put the phone down, feeling worse. For the rest of the week William immersed himself in work. He did not return Julie's calls nor did he ring Alice. His friends teased him when he told them he was not playing football, calling him 'Oldie'. He wondered why he was so gloomy. He asked himself, "Am I ill?"

After a few days, he decided what he needed was a short break. He owned a small apartment in Malaga, which was rented for most of the year but perhaps it might be vacant, with a little luck. If not, he could afford to go to a local hotel. His arrangements were almost too easy to make. He re-organised his business affairs and went shopping for new holiday clothes, the very best he could buy. In a still-gloomy mood, William headed for the airport.

He spoke to no one on the flight, which was unusual for him, but he just couldn't be bothered. The weather was as he had expected in Malaga, sunny and warm. His apartment was ready for him, and stocked with basic food by his local agent. The balcony on one side looked out over the sea, and on the other side over the pool. There were many people around, and he wondered if they were all retired, or on leave or just plain bored with life, like him.

For the next two days William did not leave the apartment. He sunbathed, played music and drank wine. He visited the local shop and bought his favourite food. He tried to convince himself that this was all he needed- a complete break from routine, and then he would return home and live contentedly. If anything, however, he was becoming even sadder and lonelier. He needed company desperately.

He envied the young fathers wrestling at the pool with cranky children. H even envied the young couples clinging together, and the older people snoozing in the sun. At least, they were together. He decided that this was not the place for him, so he hired a car and set off to explore the area. At least in the car he would be invisible, and he could stop where he liked. He was determined to stay for the full week no matter how fed up he was, though he began to feel it was even more stressful than being at home.

As he drove along, he regretted not having a golfing partner, because this seemed to be a great place for golfers. Still, he felt that he looked like a man with a purpose, who was driving along. Then he remembered the Hotel International where he had stayed many years ago with his then fiancée, who later became his wife. Anyhow he decided to stop there for lunch, and look around the place again. He remembered bringing his daughters here after his divorce and they had made so many friends and had gone out on so many trips that he had had the time to look around. He had actually bought his apartment during that visit.

He went straight to the bar to order a gin and tonic. Waiting for his change, he looked idly in the mirror opposite, and noticed a woman hugging a young man. Everyone seemed to be happy. He looked more closely, and noticed that the woman looked like was the double of Alice. Surely it couldn't be Alice, looking tanned and so pretty, and laughing and listening so intently to the man she was with.

William didn't know what to do. He wondered if should he go away and say nothing. It probably wasn't his Alice anyhow. This woman was more vibrant and attractive. Heads were turning to look at her, and she seemed looked so happy and alive. Alice had not mentioned going on holiday, and surely she would have said so? Then William remembered that he had not allowed her to do much talking anyway.

The couple were now going outside to the poolside tables; but yes it *was* Alice. He knew by the way she moved. Was she mad? How dare she lead him on, and then appear with a stranger like this? He was full of resentment and – he had to admit it – he was also jealous. What should he do? Of course she owed him nothing, no loyalty, though they had slept together on a few occasions. Also he had been seeing Julie, whom Alice didn't know about. Still she could have said something to him about what she was doing. It was disgraceful to see a woman of her age playing the field. She should have more pride in herself.

Just then he heard a voice shout, "William? Yes it is you, what a surprise! I didn't know you were here. When did you come?" It was Alice on her feet, and coming towards him. He hoped she wouldn't feel sorry to see him alone. He wanted to pretend he hadn't seen her, but he could not help himself. He jumped up and said, "Alice, what a surprise! Imagine you being here. I had some business to attend to with the apartment, so I just dashed over for a few days. I'm going home on Saturday."

"Why so am I," she said, "I come here two or three times a year to visit my lovely son and his family. I have now bought myself a little place in the sun."

The young man was now coming towards them, handsome and smiling. "This is my son Sam," he heard Alice say. He could feel relief surging through him. She was free, she was still his Alice. Amid the introductions, he heard himself agreeing to meet Alice, Sam and his partner and little girl for dinner in the hotel that evening. In fact, Sam was the assistant manager.

William said his goodbyes, and rushed off to change, take a shower, and later to buy some flowers for his Alice. Why did he keep calling her 'his' Alice? He realised with a shock that that was how he thought of her. She was so full of life, and there was yet another side to her to that he hadn't bothered to find out about. She also excited him, and made him feel jealous. But he must be careful. His feelings might have been heightened just by being out there by himself. He wondered if he would feel the same about Julie when he got home. After all, he was nearly fifty, his life was good, and why had felt so miserable? Yet he realised somewhere deep inside himself that he had no one to share his life.

Later that evening, as he raised his glass, he thought that Alice's soft face looking at him across the table at him full of love and friendship was the best thing to happen in his life for a long time. "Yes," he thought, "she will do me well."

Then through a haze of love, wine and food, he heard Alice say, "William, I was talking to Julie before I came out. She was asking about you." William had been playing around with both of them, but had never known that Julie and Alice were old friends. He could feel his face suddenly drain. What on earth would he do now? The playboy had played one game too many.

A Post Too Far

One of the joys of being retired is the calmness of the mornings. Once you accept the fact that you are no longer a cog in the economic welfare of your country, you can be a road-walker when everyone else is fast asleep or you can potter in your dressing-gown viewing daytime television, or you can stay in bed and do all your business from there.

The choice is yours and for the first few months I thoroughly enjoyed myself, until I became bored, and a feeling of uselessness began to set in. So I began to rethink my mornings and I reached a compromise. I decided to rise reasonably early, to get dressed, to put on make-up and to take myself out – maybe to church or maybe not, but definitely out! So now I find myself in another routine, going to church on certain days, seeing friends for coffee and going to meetings, having become involved in too many organisations. We are all creatures of habit, and we have a need to be useful and to be involved.

Since I have begun this healthy lifestyle I have been amazed at some of the early morning activities which I was unaware of until now. My once quiet road is actually a hive of activity, and one would almost need to book a time to go for a solitary walk. I noticed one rather portly pair who were panting along the road every morning, and were dressed in matching outfits.

I noticed that married couples out walking do not talk or look around them. They just pound along. Usually one of them takes the lead, while the other seems red-faced and in distress. People who walk alone always look happier and more at ease. Perhaps I am just jealous of all these people, as I can no longer go for a walk because of operations on my knee.

However, I have had my own morning adventure. I *have*. As I picked up my morning paper, which is delivered to my home, I saw through the glass door two large sacks which were standing beside my front doorstep. My first thought was that I had received a delivery of coal, but I then remembered that I hadn't ordered coal, so what was in these strange sacks?

I opened the door and, full of curiosity, I put my hand into the sack nearest me. To my surprise I pulled out a parcel addressed to a neighbour up the road. I dropped the package like a hot potato back into the sack, and quickly closed the door. I went into the kitchen, put on the kettle and decided I wouldn't look out again for a while. I felt I had done something illegal. An hour later, however, I plucked up the courage to look outside again, and to my amazement, the sacks were gone.

My curiosity deepened, and the next morning I was peeping out of my windows from seven o'clock in the morning, and two sacks were left on my doorstep again, when I was in the bathroom. This was a secret which I could keep no longer. I told various friends about what was happening, but I knew by their faces they didn't know what to believe. They said: "The Royal Mail wouldn't do something like that, they couldn't do that". Someone else said, "Report it to the authorities", but I couldn't do that. I didn't want someone to get into trouble.

So, just to prove that this was really happening, I brought my neighbour over to see them one morning – to see the sacks which were being dumped on my doorstep. She started to laugh and she said, to me: "I thought you were running a catalogue business when I saw the big post van stopping and the postman carrying the sacks to your house every other morning."

I was at a loss what to do; despite having these sacks dumped mysteriously at my front-door each morning, I really didn't want to get anyone "the sack", so to speak. However, I eventually decided to take a photograph of the sacks, because I felt that it was important to have pictorial proof that I was being left in charge of the Royal Mail every morning.

After a while, I discovered that the post had its own patterns of delivery. I came to know the days the post was light, and I found myself looking at post-boxes and examining the collection times. However, it was the wet mornings that worried me the most. I actually found myself lying awake listening to the rain, peeping out at the sacks, and wondering should I pull the bags into the porch in case somebody's mail got wet. The whole episode was making me lose sleep; I was becoming obsessed with the post, above all things! I was actually prowling around in the mornings, trying to catch the Santa Claus postman, but without success.

Then one morning there were no sacks on my doorstep. The dumping of this mail had ended as mysteriously as it had begun. I actually felt angry, and asked myself, "What has happened?" I couldn't believe how involved I had become. Now there was nothing I had to get up early for. I felt bereft for a few days, until I read a tiny article in the local newspaper. The stark heading made me shiver. It stated: "*HOUSEHOLDER CHARGED WITH TAMPERING WITH THE ROYAL MAIL.*"

I read it twice to make sure it wasn't me. But it could have been so, and who would have believed my story? I never found out by whom or why the sacks were left at my door, but I have the photos to prove that for two months I worked for the Post Office – and that is my secret!

Chance Meeting

It was 1977 and I was teaching in a primary school in one of the most bombed towns in Ulster. We had moved from London and were just getting settled in when the Troubles broke out. It was a worrying time, trying to give the children some freedom while at the same time being aware of the dangers.

We lived up a steep hill, so we had a wonderful view of the valley and the mountains in the distance. After London we loved it. There were some drawbacks, too, because we always knew when our poor town was in trouble. We could see the smoke and the flames. We always felt safe up on our hill, until one Sunday evening I well remember, when we woke to really loud gunfire. The noise and the flashes seemed to roll around the house. We tried to keep calm and we gathered the children into the hall, wrapped ourselves in duvets and sat it out.

The noise was appalling, and inside I thought it was never going to end. In fact, it lasted for an hour, but for us it did take all night to get everyone back to bed and reassure the children into sleep. Next morning we heard that three men had been killed in the local graveyard on the hill opposite us. We were told they had been hiding guns. One of them who had been at school with my son, was sixteen. His brother had also been killed – he was seventeen. Of course there was an older man with them, and he had also been killed. It was a very emotional and upsetting time for our community. My school remained open, but most of the children were kept at home. The funerals were frightening with standoffs between the police, soldiers, and the mourners. I taught sisters and friends of the deceased so we had to attend the wakes. There seemed to be no end to grief and misery during that long winter.

The following July we decided to go to London for our holidays. We visited our old neighbours in Harrow and we went sightseeing for the benefit of the children, and while we were there we were invited to a dinner-dance in Kensington Town Hall, held by my husband's old football club. It was an enjoyable evening. The food was good and the music was great. My husband got caught up with all his old team going down memory lane so I decided to go downstairs to watch the dancing and to be with the other women.

We were all sitting, talking and laughing, when a tall, quite handsome, man came over and asked me to dance. He was a very good dancer and talker. He told me he was a soldier, a captain in the Army, home on leave, and divorced, and his friends had persuaded him to come with them to the dinner. I, in turn, told him how I had arrived at the dance. So we agreed that we might as well enjoy the dancing until one of us was 'claimed'. He was a most charming man. It sounds old fashioned, but it was hard to believe that he was a soldier. He told me he had just had a tour of duty in Ulster and he recognised my accent. We went to the bar for a drink. I was feeling quite daring and thought to myself that it served my other half right. He hadn't given a thought to me. I told him where I lived and I thought he went a bit quiet, but I chatted on. I was feeling quite flattered. Here was a great-looking man paying me attention, and I felt young and carefree. It was while we were dancing that he casually said he and his men had been involved in a bad gun-battle in Ulster. He said he had been really afraid and that it had been the worst in over twenty years of service. I couldn't help but tell him that we had had a bad experience of a gun-battle in a different way.

Amazingly, we were speaking of the same battle. He was horrified to hear that it had been our little house that had been caught in the middle. I went on to tell him what we had suffered as a community, the grief, the anger and the feeling of hopelessness about it all. We were just beginning to get down to a deeper discussion when I heard my name being called. He stood up immediately and told me what a lovely hour or so he had enjoyed. It was with some secret regret that I said my goodbyes to him. "We may meet again you never know," he said as he gave me a peck on the cheek and walked over to his friends.

My husband was quite merry, and continued to talk non-stop about how the boys all remembered how he had captained them to success. "That's two captains I've met tonight," I thought to myself. The holiday in London passed quickly, and soon we were home and the new term was upon us. Ulster was the same as usual – dismal news and dismal weather. I often thought about my meeting with the soldier in London, and the coincidence of him being in charge of the army in my town. I didn't dare tell anyone except close friends and family. It would have been too dangerous.

One cold afternoon on my way home down the main street, I saw a group of soldiers coming towards me. As was usual I took no notice, as did everyone. Suddenly I was aware of the group breaking up and taking cover in shop doors and entries. Then I heard a voice say, "Excuse me, but I believe we met in London." I looked, and there in front of me was my dancing partner in full uniform. I noticed he had leather gloves on, and carried a small cane. I was absolutely shocked and frightened. There I was in the main street surrounded by soldiers while the one in charge engaged me in friendly conversation. I managed a nod, and a "yes". Then I mumbled something like: "I'm glad you're well, but you must know I cannot talk to you here." Already people were beginning to look at us.

He nodded, smiled and said, "I apologise, but I just wanted to say hello." I turned and started to walk away as fast as I could. When I got home I felt mean and awful. Vanity made me look in the mirror, and I looked like a drowned rat. How could he have recognised me?

Next day when classes were over and I was marking books in the classroom, our school cleaner came in to see me. She said, "Mrs T, my daughter was down town yesterday and saw you being questioned by the army. So we were wondering were you alright?"

She stood there waiting for an answer. I smiled at her and said, "He thought he knew me, but it was just a case of mistaken identity." Sometimes truth is stranger than fiction.

TOMMY THOMPSON

The Oilman's Wife

As a television technician, my service area was mainly concentrated around East Belfast but there were some call-outs to other places. "Be there for 2.00 pm sharp," ordered the TV rental company staff, as I collected my repair schedule for the day. After a delay in the city it was past 3.00 pm before I rang the bell of a large modern bungalow not far from Belfast.

A tall, very attractive, 30-something female opened the door. "You're late," she said in a mildly chiding tone, but with a warm, welcoming smile. I was expecting you much earlier." Whatever her expectations, I was ill-prepared for the vision confronting me. She was blonde, dressed or rather semi-dressed in the briefest skirt I had ever seen, revealing long blue-patterned stockings. The Sixties was the era of the minis – including Mary Quant miniskirts as well as motor cars! My customer had obviously embraced the fashion with enthusiasm. Her upper attire was equally sparse, in an off-the-shoulder blouse with a deep cut which was nearer her hemline than her chin. Despite the brevity of her apparel, she was not tarty, and radiated an aura of elegance and cultured affluence.

"Come with me," she said. As I followed down a long corridor, in her wake an intoxicating perfume enveloped me. An earlier childhood nursery rhyme came to my thought: "Come into my parlour said the spider to the fly!" Thankfully, I was led to the faulty television and started work immediately. It was a major job requiring dismantling, and I had to use the floor as a workbench. During the fault-finding procedure the young lady also sat on the carpet, in close proximity to me. Her nearness, compounded by the overpowering perfume and skimpy attire, was interfering with my concentration. As a deterrent, I deliberately discharged several unnecessary but spectacular 12,000 volts sparks from the cathode ray tube. In fright, she retreated to a less distracting position.

While I was carrying out the repairs, she talked freely about her domestic life. Her husband was a technician in an off-shore oil depot.

It was a well-paid job, providing a comfortable life style, but he was only home on leave twice a year. "This is a quiet, backward town," she explained. "I often feel very lonely and bored." Shortly afterwards, she left the room and soon returned with a tray of tea and scones. I took a break from work, and the chat continued. Almost knee-to-knee together on the carpet, it was a disconcerting position, due to her nearness and an embarrassing display of stockings, suspenders and bare shoulders. I could not address her face-to-face. My conversation had to be pitched to a point some three feet over her head. "That's strange," she remarked suddenly. "Do you always put two spoonfuls of strawberry jam in your tea?" In my confusion I had mistaken the jam dish for a sugar bowl. I quickly salvaged my dignity "All the time," I explained. "Did you know that strawberry jam is packed with vitamins?" The conversation and the tea-break stretched on, but without any further intake of strawberry jam.

"Do you dance?" she asked me suddenly. Before I could reply she continued, "My female friend and I go dancing every Saturday night. She's divorced and lonely like myself." I explained that I had not danced for some time. "Don't worry," she assured me. "We'll look after you, and you will have a good time."

I was only 27, and the prospect of being chaperoned by two man-hungry predatory women had for me the elements of fantasy or potential disaster – especially as I was only recently married. However, not wishing to appear ungrateful, I made a non-committal reply. My technical training had not prepared me for such developments, but I was doing my best. Despite the distractions, the TV repair was almost completed but a final inspection revealed that there was some 'ghosting' in the picture. This was a condition normally produced by aerial misalignment.

The aerial, however, was in the roof space and Blondie, as I now called her, directed me to the ceiling trapdoor in the bathroom. I stood on the cistern and dragged myself up into the roof-space. The problem was soon obvious – it was bent reflectors on the aerial array, which I soon corrected. I climbed back down whilst trying to replace the trapdoor. My feet slipped off the cistern, and I crashed to the floor, half stunned – both legs were trapped, and one foot was numb and wet. Was it blood? My left leg was caught behind the cistern down pipe, and my right leg was firmly trapped in the 'S bend' of the toilet.

The commotion brought the young woman rushing back to the bathroom, whereupon she promptly slipped on the now-wet floor, and ended in an unladylike, embarrassing sprawl on top of me. I managed to remove my left leg from the down pipe. However, the other foot still remained jammed in the toilet, despite all my efforts to free it – assisted by Blondie who was pulling my leg literally in desperation. I suggested half-seriously: "Maybe you should call the Fire Brigade. They are used to these situations." But she showed no enthusiasm for such a course of action. "What will my neighbours think?" she asked. "How about calling a plumber instead?"

I then had a brainwave. "Have you a long sharp knife?" I asked. She replied in alarm, "You're not going to cut your leg off in my bathroom are you?"

"Of course not," I reassured her. "I can't get off the floor, but you can reach in there with the knife and cut the laces. We'll then try and withdraw my foot from the shoe."

The surreal situation defied imagination. I was sitting helpless on a wet bathroom floor, with a foot immobile in a toilet bowl, and a scantily dressed blonde female was half astride me, and cutting away at my submerged shoelaces to free the foot. Under other circumstances such intimacy might have been welcome, but not if one is wet, feeling foolish and with a foot growing more numb by the minute. However, success at last! The laces were severed, and our last combined tug on my leg extricated my foot from the shoe. The shoe then followed easily.

"I hope it's not cracked," remarked Blondie, somewhat anxiously. "I don't think so. It's probably only bruised," I assured her. She replied sharply, "I was referring to my toilet. Anyhow you can't go home like that. I'll lend you a dressing-gown while I put your trousers and socks into the spin drier."

"Not at all," I responded rather hastily. "But I can't guess what my wife will say when she sees me." Blondie's eyes narrowed. "You didn't tell me you were married," she said. "You didn't ask," I joked lamely. "Indeed, I am well-married – with five young children!"

Perhaps I had overdone it. Blondie giggled, and she obviously did not believe a word. She came back with: "Just you tell your wife and five kids that a large dog mistook your leg for a lamp post." As I gathered up my equipment and asked her to her sign the repair slip, there was a final reminder. She said "Don't forget! I'll meet you at 7.30 pm sharp on Saturday at the Co-op and you can bring me home afterwards. My friend can make her own arrangements." Thereupon, I made a quick exit and retreated along the drive to my repair van. There had been enough traumas for one day. Worse could be ahead if I lingered.

A week later, a repeat call from Blondie came to the television repair office. She said, "My television set is broken again. Can you send down the young, tall, dark, engineer who was so helpful to me last week?" What was I to do? The previous experience with Blondie had been literally too close for comfort.

Then I had a brainwave. I persuaded Sammy, a colleague from a different office to accept it on my behalf. Eventually, it transpired, he had to respond to frequent breakdowns at Blondie's bungalow, but Sammy, being the stalwart friend he was, never complained. He never let me down and Blondie presumably remained a well-satisfied customer of our television repair company – in every way!

Number 12

Number 12 in Bloomfield Street, East Belfast, was my earliest home. It was in a typical street of 'two-up two-down' terrace or kitchen houses built by the owners of nearby Bloomfield Damask Factory in 1898 for their workers. The street comprised 38 dwellings, with few amenities. Each house had an outside toilet, but no hot water. The weekly ritual of a family bath was a kettle-filled tin bath in front of an open coal fire in the living room. Cooking and lighting was done by gas.

My grandfather, James Marshall, qualified as a tenant due to his position as boiler-man in the factory only 50 yards away. A family of seven children was raised in the tiny two-bedroom house. As for most working-class people, their day-to-day existence was a struggle. To improve his lot, James left his factory job to join a shipping company as an engineer. In his absences at sea, his wife, Elizabeth, ran a little shop at Number 12 to help make ends meet. Such local enterprises were common at the time. At Number 18, the family had a thriving home bakery. The mouth-watering aroma of freshly baked soda and potato bread often enveloped the street and adjacent houses. A chimney sweep traded from Number 22, and a cobbler lived in Number 37. And in the next street, one personality kept pigs in the back yard. In two streets there were no fewer than ten shops of various types, all striving to make a living. My grandmother's shop at Number 12 never prospered. She was too generous or trusting, giving 'credit', which was often not repaid, or selling sweets to children beyond their ability to pay, because she felt sorry for them.

The hardships lifted temporarily when James came home on leave with his wages, and always with a carcase of lamb over his shoulder. How he obtained it I never found out, but the brief home-coming was an occasion for celebration, and the meat filled hungry stomachs after his long absences on the Baltic shipping runs. Too soon it all came to a tragic end, which brought greater hardships for the family at home. His ship, the *Teelin Head*, was torpedoed off the Irish coast by a German U–Boat in November 1917, and all aboard perished. Tragedy struck two months later when the eldest son, also named James, was killed in France while serving with the Royal Field Artillery. The Marshalls were not alone in their wartime loss and grief. The Lowry family at

Number 8 lost their only two sons shortly afterwards. With the main breadwinners gone, the family at Number 12 only managed with great difficulty. It was only after much perseverance that the shipping company provided a meagre window's pension to Mrs Marshall.

Fate struck another cruel blow when Mrs Marshall died of cancer in 1923. My mother, Cissie, whilst working in the Belfast Rope Works, assumed responsibility for the home and the remaining five children – a challenge enough for an adult but much more for a 16-year-old girl, who was also working full-time. This was a period of grinding poverty and endemic poor health caused by widespread under-nourishment.

As always, however, time moved on. In 1932 Cissie married Jack Thompson, my father, and they were able to retain tenancy of Number 12. My father's larger house on the Woodstock Road was available, but they could not afford the small additional rent. In due time I was born, but my mother Cissie had to return to her Rope Works job only two days later. A longer absence would have caused dismissal, which could not be contemplated by the family. It was a period of worldwide recession in the aftermath of the Wall Street Crash of 1929, and the few jobs available were poorly paid. However, they were treated like gold-dust.

By 1939 there were a further two boys and a girl, in our family. It was not a large household by some standards of the time, but in our limited accommodation, space was at a premium for sleeping and day-to-day living. Others in the area had similar, if not worse, problems. A Mrs Allen lived in the next street and her family of thirteen coped – but with much ingenuity. To her credit the children were fed, clothed and well-mannered. Local gossips said that when expecting her latest child she told the visiting church minister she had run out of names to call the new arrival. "Mrs Allen," he said: "If I were you, I would call it "Quits". She must have taken his advice, or perhaps, discovered the cause of the pregnancies, but "Quits" was the last of the brood – and probably to the relief of John Lowry, the headmaster of the nearby Bloomfield Public Elementary School which could only take 120 pupils.

The school, in East Bread Street, was literally around the corner, and only fifty yards from Number 12. It had been an earlier National School, and it showed. The headmaster also doubled as odd-job man, tending the primitive coke boiler or stranding precariously on the desks to light the gaslight mantles on dark winter mornings. With four classes in one room alone, the 3-Rs were sacrosanct, as were complex mental arithmetic and essay compositions. School children today give strange looks if asked about the parsing of English grammar. What is a personal pronoun? "Eh? Is that a new kind of Walkman?" would be a typical reaction.

Our family lived in often near-destitute conditions. My father obtained occasional work on "Outdoor Relief", a Government scheme of public works. Instead of cash, a voucher worth fifteen shillings (75p) was received. This was exchanged at a local grocer's for food. My mother made her own contributions by improvising for essentials. We would join the long queues at the Co-op's main bakery to buy cheaper out-of-date bread. Wool to knit jumpers or dresses was obtained by purchases from travelling ragmen, or old discarded garments. These were washed, then unravelled, and made ready for re-knitting. Flour bags, dyed and sewn together, made useful bed sheets. 'Recycling' started longer ago than you might expect.

Another tactic my mother used was thinly-disguised begging. A stranger would be stopped at the street corner with a request to change two half-pennies for a penny to feed the gas meter. Often a generous passer-by would oblige, and not accept the smaller coins in the first place. Expediency had precedence over pride. In common with our neighbours, only in extreme circumstances would a doctor be called, as many of them required payment. 'Old wives' cures of poultices or other vile remedies were widely used instead, to bring relief to the suffering.

It was not surprising that my father, a mild-mannered person, developed strong Socialist views, which he retained even as times improved. He believed, quite correctly, that the Unionist establishment had done little to improve either Protestant or Roman Catholic living-conditions. On one occasion my mother visited the home of a Unionist councillor who was also a Justice of the Peace. A signature was needed for my father's job application. At the front door of the house she received a torrent of abuse from the councillor's wife. "How dare you knock this door? There is a door at the side for people like you." My mother poor, but proud, was humiliated. She left in tears, empty-handed.

At another time, she appealed to the Belfast Board of Guardians – another relief agency – and she was turned down for any benefit.

To add insult to the rejection, the Chairman, another leading Unionist councillor's wife, asked coldly, "Why do you people have so many children if you can't support them?" At the next election, however, the same politicians were brazenly appealing for votes. A legacy of those arrogant times still exists. Critics often refer to the rump of the old 'Fur Coat Brigade'.

The Protestant-Catholic issue never incurred strong feelings at Number 12. Indeed we felt rather sorry for them, as the Catholics we knew seemed worse off than ourselves, due to the larger families they had to raise. The priests seemed to have more power on their private lives than our ministers, and we knew that Catholics were not allowed to eat meat on Fridays. However, neither did we, as we could not afford it. Apart from any religious differences, as kids we seemed to have more fun. There were always plenty of marching bands, bonfires, Sunday School trips to the seaside on steam trains, as well as the annual Twelfth parades and also the deafening resonance of the weekly ritual of Lambeg drum-beats around the streets on Saturdays.

Despite whatever anxieties or secret tears our parents may have shared, our childhood was a happy experience. Wholesome food was always on the table, somehow. An old well-scrubbed table in the kitchen/living-room once a week became a baking-board for delicious homemade apple tarts and soda bread. Many years later the same table served as a work bench for my radio and TV business. Kids' expectations then were modest. Street games, now unheard of, were the normal activity. Youth clubs and church organisations such as the Boys' Brigade and Scouts and other healthy outdoor activities were plentiful. As well, there were the 'pictures', in often flea-pit cinemas that provided cheap escapist entertainment for children and parents alike.

A fashionable interest in the period was spiritualism, which had various venues around Belfast. Partly from curiosity and hoping to learn news of a brother, who had emigrated to New Zealand many years earlier, and who may have since died, my mother was a regular visitor with friends. As this seemed an interesting diversion from playing football, a school pal and myself attended a few of these séances. The one in an upstairs room of a café opposite the Belfast Technical College was the most spooky in atmosphere. One evening we found the service rather boring and decided to augment the séance with some surreptitious tappings and groans in the darkness. The audience's response was encouraging, but the medium was not impressed. We were ejected into College Square East with a competence that would have done justice to a club bouncer.

During the Second World War, air-raid shelters along our street were a popular play ground, as we raced the length of the street along the roofs, oblivious to the danger of a three-feet gap between each structure. Some of my more worldly-wise class mates found another use for the shelters. They played a strange game called "Doctors and Nurses." My allocated role was to act as a lookout for suspicious parents. Later when I was a little wiser about what really was going on, it was too late. The air-raid shelters had been demolished, and the girls had gone elsewhere!

In 1939, when war was declared my father found his first permanent job in the Belfast shipyard – a dangerous and tough one, but a source of regular, if poor, pay. It was a fascinating period to grow up in, although the air raids themselves were a terrifying experience. Endless nights were spent in our small and packed shelter, lit only by candlelight with scarpering cockroaches as non-human company. The smell of cats pee and other unmentionable odours was enough to persuade some neighbours to go back into the open street and to chance the bombs or anti-aircraft shrapnel. The street was surrounded on all sides by industrial complexes – which made the area a prime target zone for the German Luftwaffe bombers. The Rope Works and the surrounding streets were severely damaged in the 1941 Blitz. Many residents were killed, only two streets away from our home, when their air-raid shelter suffered a direct hit from a parachute mine. The strongest impact on us, however, was the destruction of Mr Miller's chip shop at the top of our street. We children could never forgive Herr Hitler and the Germans for that!

There were other, albeit morbid diversions, in the local community. When a neighbour passed away it was customary for everyone, including children, to call at the grieving household. Requests would be made to see the deceased in the coffin. Afterwards, there would be sleepless nights recovering from the event. In the context of dying, another curious custom was prevalent throughout the city. In Bloomfield Street the official undertaker's standby was Mrs Brown at Number 27. Her job was to wash and prepare the recent dead prior to his arrival. Then there was the inevitable 'wake'. Protestant ones were said to be less exuberant than those held by Catholics, and for some mourners this was a disappointment. However, there was always the pub after the funeral. These practices have largely disappeared. Death today is more sanitised, and less of a shared community experience, and perhaps all the better for it.

One family was troubled but harmless. There were broken marriages, with spouses returning to the parental home, and also a spoiled grandson. When errands were required, an inside wall would be hammered. This shopping signal was traditionally answered by the eldest boy in the house, but no one minded. On a good day's grocery collection, a generous one shilling (5p) would be earned. The downside of the arrangement was that the errand boy often had to fetch sweets – always Mars bars for the grandson.

The house next door, Number 10, was a source of inspiration to me. Young Bobby, played the piano accordion, and very well too. I would often spend much time with an ear close to the dividing wall absorbing his music. Such eavesdropping was hardly necessary, however, as he played so loudly. This caused my parents considerable annoyance, and more so later when we bought our first wireless set, as it was difficult to hear the programmes. However, I lapped it up. Years later when Bobby was due for his annual change of instrument, he kindly let me buy his old one, which I paid through monthly instalments. Sadly, in later years he abandoned the accordion as he believed it was inconsistent with his newly embraced religious belief as a Jehovah Witness. My present association with the accordion goes back to those early days when the toe-tapping rhythms of the "Teddy Bears' Picnic" or "Whistling Rufus" reverberated around the wall of Number 12, from their origin next door. Music was never far away in our own house. My mother, when she was not singing during her household chores, would often play her mouth-organ. At weekends, after my father had a few pints of Guinness, he would also entertain us with the only two songs he could remember.

After the post-war victory of a Labour government in Britain, living conditions for working-class families slowly improved, and the poverty began to recede. There was new hope in the air as my mother still had her daily char-woman jobs, and I had started work at fourteen years of age. Around that time, a casual remark by an old school chum about something called a "Cat's Whisker" grabbed my curiosity. In no time, I was hooked on building crude radio sets. Our backyard was festooned with various aerials which caused much alarm from our neighbours who were concerned about lightening strikes. My mother was also concerned in case I fell off the ten - foot wall when putting them up. However, that teenage hobby later provided me with a secure and well paid career of 36 years in TV and civil aviation electronics.

In 1951, fate had another cruel twist at Number 12. I contracted T.B. which at the time was rife, and often fatal. For four months prior to admission to hospital, I was kept in semi-isolation in the house. Our parents and the other two boys and a girl between the ages of fourteen and seventeen had to share the only other small bedroom. The consequential loss of my earnings for eighteen months before recovery, as well as the emotional distress and concern for my life, must have been a tremendous burden for my mother and one she carried, mainly alone, and without complaint.

Eventually I left Bloomfield Street to begin a new life with my wife, May, in Bangor but in fact little seemed to have changed. As we both worked in Belfast, Number 12 remained the focus of our activities. A £13 car I bought (with no guarantee!) created a greater bond as my parents, wife and I would visit places they had only read about. Our links with Number 12 grew, rather than diminished. Indeed our two baby sons took their first faltering footsteps on the same kitchen floor which had witnessed my own attempts to walk.

However, dark days lay ahead. In 1976, my mother Cissie was diagnosed with a terminal condition. There was disbelief and shock. It seemed so cruel. My parents were in their twilight years. Poverty and struggle were in the past, they were surrounded by a loving extended family, and they were looking towards a peaceful and secure future. The ensuing six months was a most distressing period for us all. My mother bore her suffering with her usual fortitude, and there was no self-pity. One of my most treasured possessions is a tape-recording I made of her playing her beloved mouth-organ. "The Blackboard of my Heart" was the last tune she ever played. Someday I will have the courage to replay it.

Her illness continued, and neither our prayers nor medical science prevailed. On one beautiful September morning, our darkest day, she was gone. The presence which had illuminated and inspired the lives of so many people over two generations was extinguished. A few hours later, two strangers, like intruders in the night, carried a long shapeless bag from our home and placed it in an unmarked van. The most precious thing we had ever known was leaving Bloomfield Street for the last time, borne away like an item of unwanted household garbage. My father was inconsolable. Inevitably, two years later he too passed away, a broken man. Number 12 was then taken over by my sister and her husband. But it was now a shell. The soul was missing and only the memories remained.

In 1983 the Housing Executive announced a major Redevelopment Strategy to clear unfit housing in Belfast. Bloomfield and the adjacent streets were planned for demolition. Many of the old neighbours were now owner-occupiers and tearful at the prospect of losing their homes. I knew from experience in a housing association that many of the houses had potential for upgrading with grants, instead of being ear-marked for demolition. Inside a few days the Bloomfield Residents Association was set up to argue the case for a more sensitive mix of redevelopment. Number 12 became the headquarters of the campaign which had the headline catching rally cry "The Battle for Bloomfield".

Some 250 houses were involved. There were public protests, City Hall and Stormont delegations, orchestrated letters to the press, multiple Housing Executive meetings and trade unions and politicians were lobbied. We even produced a monthly residents' newsletter. After a strenuous three-year battle we succeeded, and Bloomfield Street was saved, as were some others.

Twenty years on, there are again claims that Bloomfield Street may be demolished, as it does not meet the latest housing standards, but there will be no resistance this time. The old neighbours and caring, sharing community I once knew no longer exists. The upgraded and new houses are occupied by strangers. The area's character has changed. All doors are now kept locked, day and night. Somewhere along the way things changed. Was it our fault or that of the housing authorities?

Someday Bloomfield Street, which has witnessed much tragedy, poverty and happiness, will be demolished. And like its shattered bricks, I too will move on, as I believe, to join those dear ones who have gone on before. Together we will share a more enduring, wider embracing, Number 12 and community. It will not be ravaged by disease or poverty, and the bulldozers will never threaten. Bloomfield Street is dead, but long live the memories and spirit of "Number 12".

Leaving Home

Measured in miles and time it is a long distance from Belfast to Rosslare in the Irish Republic – a six hour journey – yet it was to be one of the shortest, saddest journeys of my life. Our elder son, Thomas, was leaving to enrol in a college in Wales. He had a natural talent for art, and had successfully completed a foundation course at Rupert Stanley College, Belfast. Despite his impressive portfolio of achievements, he failed to gain admission to a Diploma Course in Sculpture at Belfast College of Art. Eventually, he secured a vacancy at Dyfed Art College in Carmarthen, South Wales.

As we drove through the barely noticed Irish countryside, en route to the Rosslare ferry, there was the normal small talk, of no consequence, which occurs often within families on routine occasions. My wife, May, did not accompany us as our youngest son, Alan, was still at school. Whatever fears or tears she may have felt at Thomas's parting, she kept well them under control. Many years later, I have still to learn how that emotional day affected her.

During our journey south, I was acutely conscious that our family had reached an emotive watershed in the course of our life together. Our child, albeit now an 18-year-old whom we had nurtured from birth through the various stages of his life – infancy; starting school, the 11-plus experience, holidays together, sickness, buying his clothes, providing pocket money for modest childhood needs, moral guidance, and other matters demanded of responsible parenthood – was now moving on. Going to a university outside Ulster would be his first tentative steps into a wider world of independence and self-sufficiency. He would be faced with challenging adjustments and moral dilemmas in a vastly different social environment. In all these, Thomas would be virtually on his own and whatever trials he met, we would probably never learn about them. My wife and I would not be near to assist or comfort him. It was a distressing prospect for a previously close-knit family to contemplate, but we had to submit to the Biblical command: *Loose him and let him go.* It would not be easy!

Obviously I could make no comments to him on the significance of the occasion as we shared an otherwise uneventful journey to Rosslare and the ferry crossing to Holyhead. Arriving at Carmarthen and the college in Wales, the formalities of enrolment were quickly completed – without my presence or assistance. After my initial concern about available accommodation, a rather austere and basic room was allocated in a Church of England Student Hostel.

My son then discovered that the Student's Union had organised a bus excursion to London for the following day, and he received an invitation to join the others on the trip. This was welcome news to me. It meant that on his first day away from home and in a strange country, he would have little time to reflect when I left for the Irish ferry. Meantime, in the afternoon I bought him a 50 cc motor-bike which was just powerful enough to help him to travel around the area but offered the minimum incentive to become a Welsh champion in the style of the Irish hero Joey Dunlop. Buying a motorbike for a son was the last thing I would have considered at home, but it was essential in this new situation. Driving tuition was also organised for him.

In the evening we booked into a Carmarthen pub for bed and breakfast. As we sat in the saloon after our meal, we were entertained by a local character, whose flow of wartime anecdotes in musical Welsh inflections passed the evening rapidly. His eloquence was probably due to the copious amounts of draught Guinness which we bought for him. In the course of his stories he mentioned that 617 Squadron, the famous 'Dambusters', had trained in Wales and that our pub had been their regular hostelry. Thomas and I shared an interest in world war history and particularly in aviation, so we greatly appreciated the Welshman's reminiscences. When he finally left it was time to retire to our upstairs room overlooking the main street. In anticipation of the next days' events it was only with difficulty that I eventually drifted off into a restless sleep

It had been arranged for the student's bus to collect Thomas outside the pub at 6.30 am the next morning. I was still half-asleep when we received the landlord's call for an early breakfast. During the meal there was only low-key farewell chat between us. It was too late for anything more profound that might betray my, or his, true feelings. For the umpteenth time he was told: "Don't forget to write, and if you are short of cash let us know." No doubt similar advice was given by many parents in the same circumstances, since time immemorial.

In the eerie stillness of that dark October morning the bus arrived at 6.30 am punctually. There was a brief interchange "Goodbye, Dad" and "Take care, Thomas" as he and two other students mounted the vehicle. It drove off down the deserted street. A faint farewell wave from behind the steamed-up bus window was the enduring image I still recall, as I leaned over our bedroom window.

The bus's fading rear lights and engine's throbbing sounds going into the distance were the trigger for my already primed emotions. It came like a hammer-blow. Our son had really gone! It was not just on a student excursion to London but the child we had known, reared and loved for years, and who had returned that love, was leaving our direct parental care forever. He was entering an uncertain future as a young adult, and in that strange lonely bedroom I experienced an overwhelming sense of sadness and loss, akin to that when my Mother and Father had passed away years earlier within a short time of each other.

There was an intense urge to escape from Carmarthen and Wales, as if a change of location would ease my pain. I had to get away. The account with the landlord was settled, quickly, and I left the pub with its previously enthralling Dambusters association. They did not seem very relevant or interesting to me any more. "To hell with the Dambusters and the World War II battles," I thought. "Today is the real world". As a final gesture I went to the Students' Hostel, and another £5 note (with further unnecessary advice in an envelope), was slipped under Thomas' door. The locked, empty room itself became another symbol of the growing break-up of our family and our separation.

The journey from Carmarthen to Holyhead ferry terminal was an emotional roller-coaster, and a heartbreaking experience. Alone in the car, I felt that a part of our family had been left behind in a 'foreign' country. At times the tears flowed unashamedly, despite it being an embarrassment to my manhood and intelligence; but when emotions are dominant, logic and realism are shut out.

I was grateful that being alone did at least provide privacy from curious witnesses' eyes. A distraught adult is not a pretty sight. The ferry sailing to Rosslare and the long drive to the Ulster border were only a little less distressing. On reaching Newry I sought out a non-vandalised public telephone, and rang my wife in Belfast. Her cheerful, familiar voice restored my thoughts to an emotional even keel, at least to some degree. It was reassuring that I was returning to a happy, loving home – albeit a little emptier, and a little quieter. Henceforth, my wife

May, and I would pray, plan and adjust for a different future and what it might unfold for us all, including our distant son in his new life.

Many people have found at times of deep emotional or even physical trauma, that the words of the American poet, John Greenleaf Whittier, offer them comfort and reassurance:

All the good the past has had
Remains to make our own time glad.

The inevitable loosening of close family ties was a challenge to us, but as time passed the wisdom of the poet's words were demonstrated to me. I realised that change should not necessarily mean loss. Happily, some twenty years on, the son I had left in Wales on that heartbreaking day is now a successful architect in Dorset, England. He makes regular visits home with his Scottish wife and three young children.

On one such visit, just as I was leaving for a weekend break in Co. Donegal, his youngest son placed his tiny hand in mine. With a trusting, even pleading look that can only come from innocence, he asked me, "Granda, when you come back from your holiday would you and Nanny take me to the Zoo to see the animals?" Suddenly, in my mind's eye, the years scrolled back. For a moment, there was an urge to shed a tear once again, but no longer in sadness. The "Dambusters" bus had returned!

The Beach

A young woman fussed around the elderly person in an invalid chair, buttoning up his cardigan and adjusting a rug over his knees. "I'll be back in ten minutes, Dad," she reassured him: "Just as soon as I collect your coat from the car. It's bound to get chilly and we haven't had our picnic yet." She addressed the little girl nearby playing in the sand, "Jenny, look after Grandpa until I return." The man pleaded, "Please, Elizabeth, don't be long. I might have another weak turn." But with an affectionate hug and a cheery wave to the two figures on the beach, she was gone.

It was a warm summer's evening and some visitors were still enjoying the season's dying fling before the approaching autumn. The invalid, acutely aware of his loneliness, apart from the happily playing five-year-old, lapsed into deeper reflection. "I did not consider a year ago I would end up in this condition," he thought bitterly, partly addressing the wheelchair. "Then, I could have swum the five miles to that island and back. Now I can't even walk or attend myself without assistance."

His memory rehearsed again, as often since, the day he faced the family doctor, who was a life-long friend. He had said, "Robert, as you know I had to refer your case to a specialist for more specific tests, and the results have just come in. I had hoped to give you encouraging news, but regrettably the outlook is serious. In fact, it's worse than that, the condition is untreatable." Robert was stunned. He had expected to hear a recommendation to ease up or take a holiday, but not this. His brain was numbed into semi-paralysis when it registered only some of the doctor's words: "Terminal . . . no cure . . . six months to live, maybe a year . . . tidy up your affairs . . ."

Robert had no recollection of driving home through heavy traffic. Each word of his doctor's verdict pounded like a hammer blow pounded to his head. His familiar world had collapsed. Former certainties were now worthless. His ambitions for himself and family were no longer relevant. Robert felt that he had no future, but only the sentence of a lingering painful death, and the distress of his family.

As he scanned the distant horizon out to sea, its blankness reminded him of his own diminishing frontier of existence, moving into oblivion or the unknown. There would be no more family holidays, or seeing his grandchildren grow into teenagers, no more of so many prospects . . .

In deference to his wife's wishes he had explored alternative remedies – homeopathy, crystals, dieting, faith-healing gurus, including a spiritual healing group within his own church. There was no improvement. "Bless them for trying," thought Robert. "I should be grateful. What the hell! Why am I torturing myself? Reason should have prepared me not to expect God to help me when he lets others people die, and permits wars, earthquakes and other terrible events. There is no logic. Are there two Christian Gods? Or more likely, none at all?"

"Damn it! Damn it! I don't want to die yet," he screamed into space with frustration and fear. He thumped his wheelchair, safe in the knowledge there was no one else nearby to witness his outburst. A small, soft hand touched his clenched fist. It was Jenny, his granddaughter. "Grandpa," she said. "You are not going to die. Mummy told me you were sick. Now every night before I go to sleep, we both pray that you will get well again. We love you and need you so much. Do you remember when Peter my rabbit was sick? We prayed then and saw him get better again, and Mummy said that you are more precious to God than a little rabbit." Robert felt shame at his loss of control, and, to be reminded of this by a five-year-old child. He spoke to his granddaughter: "You're absolutely right, my dear. Thank you, I'm sorry." He patted her on the head. Somewhere in his memory a long-buried quotation emerged. Was it from Shakespeare or The Bible? "And a little child shall lead them."

A sudden activity overhead drew his attention. A large flock of gannets were swooping and circling, their brilliant white plumage with black wing tips performing a graceful aerial ballet against the backdrop of a clear blue sky, and orchestrated by shrill cries as some of them dived into the sea in search of food. "Such freedom, such beauty in form," considered Robert sadly. "If only I could be as one of these instead of a sick, dying mortal racked in pain and fear."

"You can, Robert." A voice at his side startled him. "You can be free," the voice repeated. He heard no one approaching. Close by him stood a young man, who was strangely familiar. He was about 30 years old, and attired in casual holiday wear. His comforting arm embraced Robert's bowed shoulder. The stranger smiled and in a low, but clear, tone he said, "All things are possible if you only understand and believe." Robert responded curtly, almost rudely. "If you are another Bible thumping do-gooder, please don't waste your time on me. I've been along that route already. It just does not work, at least not for me. Anyhow, who are you? How do you know my name?"

"My name is irrelevant," the cryptic reply came. "But, I know you better than you know yourself. You are a good man, Robert. If it were otherwise, you could not be talking to me now."

The invalid was impressed by the stranger's knowledge of his name and the quiet confidence of his voice. He also appeared harmless. Robert relaxed. "Am I in the presence of a sympathetic passer-by?" he asked himself. Then other bizarre thoughts flashed across his mind. Perhaps he is a guardian angel or an extra terrestrial alien! The young man, as if reading his mind reassured him "You are not hallucinating. Neither am I an alien." He smiled as he spoke. "If you spare me a few minutes of your time, there are some ideas I would like to share with you." Curious by now, Robert nodded his assent.

The stranger told him, "Over the centuries, gifted individuals have reached beyond the boundaries of the physical senses and reported communication with entities in other dimensions, or levels of consciousness. Primitive man experienced rapport with nature spirits or divas; others with fairies and their kindred variations – your Irish 'wee folk'. Mystics and prophets from Christian and so-called Eastern pagan traditions had spiritual revelations, and in recent times communion with guardian angels and alleged aliens are being claimed. These are only a small sector of the arcane phenomena which defy your rational explanation. In an opposite camp, whilst physicists draw the line about life forms beyond the physical world, credible voices are postulating that there must exist parallel or multi-dimensions which can only satisfy current quantum physics theories on the structure of matter and time.

However, beyond the two opposing positions – the tentative dabbling by men into the uncharted nether regions of the human mind, or the modern scientist in the laboratory formulating advanced theories about the nature of the universe – there is an infinitely higher level of existence; a universal power or mind. It is the ultimate reality where matter and time do not exist at all."

Robert found this hard to follow, but the stranger continued: "Visionaries and mystics describe their revelations as glimpses of a dynamic, intelligent life source and a loving, omnipotent spiritual consciousness filling all space. They experienced an all-embracing power that knew only harmony and love – good and immortality. Death as the antithesis of life cannot exist there. It is certainly not the soulless mechanical model of quantum wave energy proposed by the physicists. Based on their concept of enlightenment, early spiritual teachers like Jesus Christ, the Buddha and others, founded movements to share and propagate the good news or gospel. This was the true meaning of life and its purpose. Some of these works included the raising of the dead. Ultimately, however, the clammy hand of human vanity, and man-made organisation stifled the essence of the original teachings, leaving instead a hollow shell of ritual and religious dogma. This was a cruel caricature of fundamental Truth."

Robert listened with fascination to the stranger's words. These ideas were radical, indeed revolutionary, but were they merely the rantings of another drugged brain? Nevertheless, they carried a ring of authority, and there were some aspects he could accept. The speaker continued:

"Over the centuries, although revelations of universal spiritual truth have been obscured from time to time by decadence or false doctrine, it cannot be suppressed entirely. It is available today for dedicated searchers and those seeking beyond the cynicism and materialism of the age. Robert, be as the Prodigal Son. Strive to return to your natural spiritual home or consciousness. You will be well rewarded with knowledge of your true identity as a child of the infinite cosmos. You are an integral part of it. It is your destiny. Nothing can deny you it but yourself. Claim your inheritance. In it you will find wisdom, freedom and healing."

Robert at last spoke out: "Who are you? Why are you telling me such strange ideas?" The young man replied, "Robert, you and I are one. I am your real higher selfhood, and we are one with our Father, Creator. Call it what you will – God: Allah, Brahman and others. Such titles are merely convenient human concepts." The speaker's voice began to fade. Robert, in astonishment witnessed the young man's body beginning to dissolve into transparency. Behind the fading outline distant objects came into view. A disembodied voice in barely audible tones was heard "Robert, do not cling to illusion. Claim your birthright. You will find a new sense of infinite love and spirit. In it there can be no natural disasters; hatred; warfare and disease, or even death – only seek, believe and prove it for yourself – and others."

Robert was alone again. He was aware of an inexplicable sensation of loss and sadness. Something wonderful, if indescribable, had touched him. Now it had gone, before he had time to unleash the dam of questions built up inside him. That moment was replaced by an overwhelming awareness of an inner light – a brightness increasing in intensity but, soothing. No longer conscious of his frail body, he was detached and floating towards the light source. An unspeakable feeling of joy and tranquillity enveloped him. His old, tired world had passed away. He was coming home to claim his rightful place in the living, eternal cosmos. Was it purgatory, nirvana or heaven? Did it matter what humankind called it. Here was his destiny. It awaited him.

Robert's reverie was suddenly disrupted. Jennifer was tugging at his sleeve. "Grandpa, wake up." A minute elapsed before he adjusted reluctantly to his old surroundings. "Why did I have to come back to this miserable existence?" he thought. Apart from the child, he was still alone. The young man must have existed only in his drug-fuelled imagination. But there was a difference. His senses had acquired an acute, higher level of perception beyond the normal human awareness. All the previous ugliness and irritations of everyday activity were transformed. An underlying sense of beauty, love and purpose pervaded everywhere and all things. An aeroplane and its contrail high in the sky embodied the intelligence and aerodynamic principles that could lift man above a limiting native element to travel through space.

The flowers on a promenade stall radiated a vividness and variety of beauty with a freshness never seen before. Heavy traffic rolled along the nearby road in courteous, disciplined procession. At a zebra crossing a stranger patiently escorted a pensioner with his zimmer over the road. A teenager's ghetto-blaster earlier churning out loud, toneless noise was now relaying softer, richer harmony. Life indeed, could be a sweet, carefree experience. Was this new elevated consciousness an insight of the ultimate reality the imaginary stranger had described with such conviction and authority? Jennifer was tugging Robert's sleeve again. "Grandpa! You're not listening. Could I have an ice cream please?"

The beach had just cleared of day trippers. Threatening dark clouds and white horses whipped up by a cool sea breeze signalled the end of an idyllic visit to the coast. The sudden, almost menacing, mood of the scene only enhanced in Elizabeth her emotions of disbelief and dread. "Where are my ill father and daughter? They just can't disappear in daylight among crowds." Her panic increased as she saw the overturned invalid chair and scattered picnic items. She scanned the beach for help. She was alone, apart from the black and white birds circling overhead. "It's my fault, I should not have left them. Maybe they are drowned or even kidnapped," she thought as grief and guilt embroiled her.

Unable to consider her next actions, she ignored the shouting from the promenade. This time another call. "Elizabeth! Elizabeth!" echoed clearly around the promenade wall. Two people drew closer, the taller guiding a child's bicycle. As they came nearer, she exclaimed in disbelief: "It can't be. One is Jenny; the other looks like my father. It's impossible. He's ill and has not walked for months." The man lifted the bicycle and child effortlessly down to the beach, but he was not the crippled person she had left sometime earlier. It was a fit, younger looking version of the man she had tended over many months.

"Hullo, Elizabeth." It *was* her father! "I hope we did not worry you?" he apologised. "I took Jennifer off for an ice-cream." Almost speechless with shock, and in a mixture of tears and joy, she embraced her father almost violently.

"Dad, I thought you were both . . . you've changed . . . What is happening to us, are we hallucinating?"

"Elizabeth, dear," Robert responded in strong resonant tones not heard in a long time. "I *have* changed and it's a miracle. Soon after you left me I had a friendly visitor. He shared with me many strange but inspiring ideas which at first seemed obscure and then began to ring true. Eventually I dozed off in his presence – it was very rude of me, I know. I then had a wonderful dream. When Jennifer awoke me he was gone. I was then aware of an overwhelming sensation of freedom and strength. There was life in my limbs. My old vitality and clarity of mind had returned to normal. I had felt so self-conscious sitting in a wheelchair. When Jennifer asked for an ice-cream I overturned it in my haste to leave it. It was only as we walked along the Promenade the experience hit me hard. I was cured. The disease which had been eating away the remainder of my life and distressing all of us had vanished.

Elizabeth, I can't explain what happened today or why it should be me. I've had the most traumatic experience of my life, and thankfully it has been a happy one for us all. There must be a purpose. I'm sure it will become clearer in the days ahead. In the meantime, let us go home, give thanks and celebrate this remarkable day."

The small group gathered up their possessions and headed for the distant car park. Robert paused briefly to look back at the deserted beach. A strange silence had descended on the scene. Nearby traffic sounds were muted. Sea waves lapped noiselessly over rocks and sand. A surreal, tangible stillness and peace engulfed the scene. Then the moment was abruptly shattered by the sound of seabirds. Overhead a flock of gannets hovered, almost stationary. The largest peeled away to dive directly towards Robert. He stood frozen to the spot, neither afraid nor surprised. The bird completed several circuits around him, its flapping black wing tips only feet away from his face. Uncannily, almost human-like cries were heard before the gannet soared upward to rejoin the waiting flock. With a final crescendo of cries, the birds rapidly disappeared from view. Robert was nonplussed. Birds cannot communicate in human terms, but what he thought he heard suggested otherwise. "Welcome home. You are now like us – always were, always will be. You are free!"

Jennifer grabbed his hand and dragged him away. "Grandpa, did not I tell you that you are more precious to God than my silly little rabbit?" Robert replied gratefully, "Indeed you did, dear child. I only believed you then, but now I know."

Waiting For A Train

The summer of 1979 was a milestone period for our railway preservation society. The Belfast and County Down Railway Museum Trust had been established two years earlier to re-open a section of the former rail network between Ballynahinch and Rowallane Gardens, Saintfield. The old B.C.D.R. system, with the exception of the Bangor branch line had shut down in 1950. For an aspiring working museum the society's artefacts collection was sparse. A passenger carriage had been purchased from a Comber farmer. It had been used as a hen house for twenty-five years and is showed! He claimed Queen Victoria had used it during her Jubilee visit to Belfast in 1897. We were sceptical about its Royal association, but it was our first major acquisition, although it lacked bogies or wheels and rested on concrete blocks. Apart from the derelict carriage/hen house, voluminous documents, photographs and the protracted negotiations with local farmers to buy back their plots of the former track bed and a vandalised station, the project was making little real progress.

The breakthrough came with tentative discussions with C.I.E., the Republic's transport agency. They agreed to donate a redundant, 13-ton brake wagon in good condition. These were a feature of many railway freight services as an auxiliary braking-aid. It would be delivered by rail from Drogheda to Northern Ireland Railways (N.I.R.) freight depot at Adelaide, Belfast and from there the Society would have to organise transport by road to our temporary storage at the D.O.E. maintenance yard outside Ballynahinch. This formidable challenge was resolved when an approach to the Army H.Q. in Lisburn proved successful. As a training exercise and a community relations gesture they would allocate a squad of Royal Engineers and the necessary equipment to move the wagon free of cost to the society.

On the big day, an impressive array of military personnel and vehicles had assembled at the N.I.R. railway depot. Another committee member and myself were present to liaise with the Army and others. The brake wagon awaited us – this was our own complete piece of rolling stock and it even had its own wheels! The initial removal operation, as befitting professionals, was executed safely and smoothly. Two 15-ton mobile cranes with slings hoisted the wagon off the rails onto a 40-

foot low loader vehicle. The wagon secured, the low loader and the accompanying escort were made ready for the final leg of the journey via Belfast and Saintfield Road to Ballynahinch.

The cavalcade that emerged from the Adelaide onto the roads of Belfast was a magnificent spectacle. Nine other vehicles accompanied our precious wagon, poised prominently on its low loader. An R.U.C. Land Rover preceded the procession, followed by two army land rovers as protection against possible I.R.A. attack. Next was a British Telecom crew van to move overhead telephone lines that might obstruct the high cranes. Secure in the convoy's centre was the wagon on its carrier. Following along in the rear were two cranes, an Army Land Rover, an R.U.C. vehicle and an Army staff car. The rare sight revived a chord in my memory – it resembled the Chipperfield Circus that had rolled through Belfast the previous year!

My car, which would have joined the line up, was diverted elsewhere. Roy, my museum colleague, who was on his lunch break, required a lift back to his office at the Housing Executive in downtown Belfast. This was a dilemma for me because as sole society representative I had to maintain contact with the removal operators. A calculated gamble was made. The convoy had just moved off on its slow 10 M.P.H. travel through Belfast. Roy could be dropped off at his work. By my estimates I would still have time to rendezvous with the vehicles six miles outside Belfast, on the Saintfield Road. Without mishap, I arrived at the projected meeting point near a garage on the main road.

Then another dilemma arose! Was I ahead of the convoy or had it already passed? Another opinion would be useful. I drove into the garage forecourt and entered the shop. A pleasant young assistant greeted me. It did occur to me that few people would know what a brake-wagon was, especially in a garage. I would have to keep it simple.

"Maybe you could help me," I said. "Have you seen a train passing in the last 15 minutes? There should be one passing this way." His smiling features took a startled look, before replying: "Well ah! Ah! I've been very busy actually and it's a very busy road here. All sorts of things pass our garage, so I can't say there wasn't one. But we don't normally see many trains. Hold on, I'll ask my boss." He disappeared into an inner office and closed the door.

Through the office window the owner and the assistant could be seen in deep conversation. When they realised I had seen them, the owner flashed a broad friendly smile and gave a cheery hand wave. I responded by waving back. The assistant then smiled and waved. Not wishing to ignore him, I smiled and waved to him also. His boss then made another wave, which I had to return soon after. The assistant returned with the news. "The boss says it has not passed yet. But if you like you can have a seat until it does arrive." Such thoughtful people, I thought.

I purchased a newspaper and sat near the window to read and watch the road, for a first glimpse of the convoy. My casual glance back to the office revealed the owner on the telephone. When he saw me he became rather agitated. He managed a very sickly smile and a feeble wave of the hand. I waved back. Such friendliness was becoming somewhat embarrassing. "Do these people have no time to do anything else?" I thought. After 10 minutes and with no sign of the vehicles, it seemed wise to move on. They must have already passed and it might still be possible to catch up with them. The assistant beat me to it. He rushed and locked the shop door. He explained: "Lunch time, sir! We always close half an hour for lunch."

I started to protest. "Sorry but I must go. I will have to catch up with the train." He assured me, "You've still time, sir, the boss has just confirmed, and you saw him on the phone, it's due anytime. You must have a cup of tea while you're waiting." Re-assured I accepted the welcome cup of tea. The owner appeared and engaged me in friendly conversations about trains. He claimed he was a railway enthusiast at one time. His father has been an engine driver on *The Flying Scotsman* before the war and had been presented to the King several times. "I've no interest in trains now that they are all diesel. I prefer the old dirty steam ones. Real trains I say."

I expressed agreement on that final comment. Having put me to ease at some degree, he returned to his office. He was back on the telephone once again, and visibly more agitated. I received another sickly grimace and wave, which I felt obliged to return, but with diminishing enthusiasm. In the meantime my anxiety about the wagon convoy was increasing. Had there been a mix-up with instructions to the Army? Had the I.R.A. ambushed the convoy?

The assistant, after being called into the office, returned. He announced: "Good news for you, sir. The boss has been speaking to the stationmaster at Saintfield. Belfast informed him a passenger train has been delayed by a signals fault. That is now fixed. Your train will definitely be here in 15 minutes. Would you like another cup of tea while you are waiting?"

I decidedly did not want another cup of tea! The strange behaviour of the garage staff was worrying me, and had set alarm bells ringing in my thought. A Saintfield stationmaster – signals breakdown – a passenger train to arrive in 15 minutes on the traffic-busy Saintfield Road. Were those two guys up to some obscure stunt, or was I going mad in my middle age? The Saintfield station had closed 29 years earlier! A more sobering thought then occurred. Was it possible the men were inmates who had escaped from a mental institution and had taken over from the real owners of the business? Their behaviour was definitely not normal. That speculation was reinforced by the sudden realisation that Purdysburn Mental Hospital was only half a mile distant. But why the agitated telephone calls, humouring me, or the delayed tactics?

Then the truth dawned slowly . . . "My God! Those guys think I'm loopy!"

A terrifying vision of brawny men in white coats, probably equipped with a strait-jacket, bursting into the garage to carry me off to the 'Big House' came to me. I had to escape the scene before it was too late. The light restraining hands that the assistant had placed on me were pushed aside. With a curt "Thanks for the tea," I unlocked the shop door and dashed to my car, still in the forecourt. In seconds, with my foot hard on the accelerator pedal, and screeching tyres and roaring engine, I was away. A quick glance back revealed the garage men and a customer standing at the shop door shouting in frustration, "Come back! Come back!" I gave a cheeky hoot on the horn and waved at them. They did not wave back.

A safe distance was soon placed between the garage and me. As I passed the hospital main gates, an ambulance with flashing lights and siren sounding came rushing out, heading city-ward. Three men in medic uniforms occupied the front seats. I could guess where they were going but it was too late. The bird had flown!

A short wait at a nearby lay-by proved successful. In the distance the high jigs of cranes came into view, coming towards me – and eventually the remainder of the convoy. Two hours later, the unloading of the brake wagon was completed and it was mounted, and secured, on a bed of railway sleepers, at Ballynahinch D.O.E. depot. The 'train' was home, and ours. The entire cost of the removal for all involved must have been considerable. Our contribution was a modest one, so on behalf of our embryo museum, I presented the senior Army officer with a bottle of Black Bush Whiskey and one dozen cans of Guinness – a bargain indeed!

Some years later I was waiting for another train – in less confusing, or threatening circumstances – as a passenger at Central Station, Belfast. There, the only white coats visible were those of the pleasant young ladies who tended the ice cream kiosk and I thought about the day when I almost became derailed!

The Mourners

It was early evening in a downtown Belfast bar as the first revellers drifted in from the street. Patrick rounded on Brian in frustration. "It's all your fault," he said. "That lot is just arriving, and we have to leave. A quid for drinks between us won't keep us here much longer. Your 'racing cert' at the horses we backed this afternoon probably never left the starting-gates."

"I'm sorry," said Brian. "I paid my barber a good fiver for that red-hot tip from the trainer's stable lad, but it proved to be a dead loss."

"Never mind that now," retorted Patrick "Here, listen to this." He had been scanning an abandoned and tattered Irish News. "I see Brendan McCrory has died. He was a remarkable man, with so many interests. He was a member of St Agnes Choral Society, of St Vincent De Paul, the GAA, and other organisations. You name it, he was in them all. Look, there are eighteen death notices in the paper. That will be some funeral! I suppose the least we can do is call and pay our respects to his family. We have enough money left for a black taxi."

Half an hour later, the Divis Street taxi deposited the two men at a large detached house in a street off the Springfield Road. Patrick warned Brian, "Keep your mouth shut. None of that nonsense such as, 'Is this the house where the dead man lives?' I'll do the talking."

In response to their knock a young man appeared. He spoke first. "I must apologise," he said. "You have come about the noise. Some friends are here and are rather boisterous. You see it's my father's wake."

"Quite the contrary," replied Patrick. "We had to drop by to show our respects to your father. It was a terrible shock to learn that poor Brendan had passed away. We were close pals over many years, since school days. In fact, I just can't believe he has gone."

"You're very kind," said the young man. "I'm Frank, the eldest. Please come and meet my mother. Old friends of dad are always welcome here."

Patrick and Brian were ushered into a large lounge crowded with people. Others were standing in a hallway or sitting on the stairs. There were about fifty altogether, and most were engaged in animated conversation against a noisy background of clinking glasses. Frank's mother was summoned to meet the new visitors.

"Patrick and Brian are old school pals of dad, mother, they're here to convey their condolences".

"We were sorry to hear about your sad loss Mrs McCrory," said Patrick. "It seems only yesterday that Brendan, bless him, and I had confirmation together."

"It's very thoughtful of you to come," replied Mrs McCrory. "If I can be heard above this noise I will introduce you to some of Brendan's relatives and friends." Faces and names soon flashed by in a blur of introductions, and were as quickly forgotten.

Then Mrs McCrory said, "You must meet cousin Edward – he is a great character, but he is the maverick of the family. He only attends weddings and funerals!" She then drifted away. Edward, a burly figure of six foot four, towered over the crowd. A large calloused hand was extended in a bone-crunching greeting. "Glad to see you guys, just call me Eddie. Hey! You're standing there empty-handed. You must join me in a drink first, and then we'll enjoy the craic and food later. That's my philosophy at these affairs. And don't look so grim. We're only at a wake. Sorry cousin Brendan," added Eddie, casting his eyes heavenward, "there's no disrespect intended."

Some time later Patrick and Brian had warmed immensely to the affable Eddie with his interminable anecdotes about his daring exploits in a travelling circus. The rapport had been well-fuelled by Guinness, with empty cans stacking up on a nearby window ledge. "I'm afraid wakes are more subdued these days", sighed Eddie. "In earlier times they were prolonged and boisterous, and lasted over the three days to ensure the deceased really was departed. There was widespread fear then of being buried alive. However, the long vigil was well-sustained with food, gossip, music and the hard stuff, usually moonshine, to keep the visitors happy in the period of mourning. Hold it! Something is happening."

Frank McCrory was standing on a chair to address the crowd. In tearful and dignified tones he thanked those present for their attendance and their expressions of sympathy. He delivered a proud tribute to his late father and his achievements in the home and community. Frank concluded: "Just before my father passed away, he told me, 'When I go, do not grieve, though miss me you may. Have a ball at my wake. Enjoy the occasion with friends. Have a few drinks and even drink my health.' Please respect my father's last wishes. Tonight should be a celebration and remembrance of a wonderful father and friend. We have ample food and alcohol. Stay as long as you wish. Cousin Geraldine here will start things going with a tune or two on her fiddle."

The crowd pulled back, and Geraldine took the floor. As appropriate for the occasion, she played a long Gaelic lament. The obsequies duly observed, she then raised the tempo with the "High Level Hornpipe" and "Dunging out Geordie's Byre". In the lounge and other rooms, dancing feet were soon responding to the lilt of the music, which grew even louder.

Ten minutes into the recital, Eddie grabbed Patrick and Brian's arms. "Come with me," he said, "You'll have to meet Brendan." The men climbed the crowded stairs. In a bedroom the deceased was laid out, dressed in his Sunday best and surrounded by Mass cards. "Doesn't he look well?" said Eddie. "He seems healthier now than when he was still with us. That week in Frank's caravan at Rostrevor worked wonders." The two visitors agreed they had never seen such a healthy corpse, and said it was a pity Brendan was dead and unable to enjoy his improved condition.

The men returned to the main assembly. A nephew, Jack, had just been asked to perform his party piece. He produced from a weathered case an equally battered accordion. Soon the rhythms of Irish and Scottish waltzes filled the air, while the audience swayed or swung their drinks in time to the music. Jack's right foot pounded the floor like a steam hammer in an accompanying beat. Other performers followed. Two neighbours produced rousing reels on a tin whistle and banjo. Another duet on mouth organ and Jew's harp ended prematurely in near-disaster, when the harp became entangled in the performer's false teeth.

The arrival of the food trolleys brought temporary a lull to the entertainment. Huge quantities of refreshments were handed around. Those who favoured a liquid diet had access to the mini-bar set up in the utility room. When the appetites and thirsts were fully sated and remnants cleared away, Frank McCrory acted as an impromptu M.C., and stood up on his chair once more. He said loudly, "Folks, you've had an early supper, and there's more to come later. Now it's your turn to earn it. Everyone should make a contribution – let's have an interesting story, or a song or your favourite joke. But remember ladies, there are gentlemen present!"

A bearded, academic type was first on his feet. He launched into an excruciatingly boring account of old Irish hiring-fairs. Eddie could not conceal his impatience, and to the visible relief of the audience, he grabbed the storyteller by the beard and dragged him to the utility room. "Have a few drinks, friend, and we'll hear the rest of your fascinating story later," he said to the startled narrator.

Eddie returned alone and the proceedings immediately livened. He belted out several bawdy songs, which were followed by jokes liberally illustrated with lurid language. The audience loved it. The spirited mood encouraged other reluctant performers to forget their inhibitions, and the songs, yarns and jokes soon flowed freely. Young McCrory gestured toward Patrick and Brian. "It's your turn lads," he said.

Patrick was confident that he was on safe ground, and he told the story of the invalid in a wheelchair who was taken to Lourdes in hope of a cure. After two Hail Mary's and the Lord's Prayer, a miracle indeed seemed to have taken place. The invalid emerged from the water with two new tyres on his wheel-chair! The story was an 'old chestnut' but it received rapturous applause, as if heard for the first time. Then it was Brian's turn. Despite Patrick's warning glare, he told a joke about a Protestant football supporter and a transvestite monk. A cool, almost hostile reaction from the audience puzzled the disappointed Brian. But the 'faux pas' was quickly forgotten as other visitors performed their party pieces.

The musicians returned, now mostly inebriated, and hardly able to stand – much less to play or to sing in tune. Three barely recognisable renditions of "Mother McCree" with backings from the fiddle and accordion players compounded the cacophony of sounds. The Jew's harp musician after retrieving his dentures, bravely attempted an unrecognisable duet with the spoons player. Geraldine, encouraged by a request, began another lament on the fiddle. After a few bars of the dirge Eddie could not contain himself: "Get that woman off," he shouted. "This is getting too much like a funeral. We're here to enjoy ourselves and celebrate Brendan." The fiddler's friend came to her aid. "I'll have you know that Geraldine's a professional musician. She has diplomas!" Eddie retorted: "I knew she had something but it sounds more like haemorrhoids to me." The fiddler and friend, miffed, retired to a quiet corner and sought solace in two gin and tonics. Eddie was still muttering, "I can't stand that 'fiddley-dee' music. Give me Johnny Cash and Dolly Parton anytime. That's real music."

Then some lighter entertainment resumed in a crescendo of noise, and dancing feet. Suddenly, above the din, angry voices had erupted near the fireplace. Joe O'Neill had Patsy McCabe by the throat in a tight grip. "How dare you make a pass at my wife," screamed O'Neill. "Apologise!" McCabe, who was literally speechless, could only gulp for air like a stranded fish. "This is disgusting, and at poor Brendan's wake, too," someone shouted.

Patsy McCabe's wife, by now incensed, lunged at O'Neill and kicked his shins. She shouted: "If my man does stray, I hope he shows better taste than that 'old bag' you have for a wife, with a face that would curdle cream. If she went to a doctor for a face-lift he would send her to a hardware store for a bag of cement to fill the cracks."

"You're not calling me an old bag," yelled O'Neill's wife as she entered the fray and grabbed at Mrs. McCabe's hair. The two women tumbled to the floor in an exchange of blows and expletives. A friend of McCabe jumped on O'Neill's back and appeared to be attempting to dislocate his head from his body. The melee quickly attracted a circle of onlookers cheering and encouraging the combatants. A beer bottle, hurled from the crowd, missed the intended target and shattered on the wall above the accordion player, who had been sitting on the floor in an alcoholic daze, trying to play a request. Unsure of his surroundings, he abruptly switched from playing the "Boys of Wexford" to "The Old Orange Flute."

Others joined in, taking sides. More bottles took flight, and soon the beer-soaked floor was a battleground of slithering angry bodies. A sobbing female emerged from the chaos. "Look at my hair. I paid £15 to have it set for tonight's wake and someone has just emptied a bowl of vegetable soup over my head." In the pandemonium Frank McCrory tried to re-assert his authority as host and M.C. but no one paid any attention, even when he threatened to call the police. The situation was clearly out of control.

An incessant loud knocking at the front door somehow penetrated above the racket. Frank opened the door to reveal Father Matthews on the threshold. The priest anxiously asked, "Is it safe to come in? I've come to discuss the funeral arrangements." Eddie, cunningly assessing the situation, acted promptly. He dived into the crowd and hauled out the two main combatants by the scruff of their necks. "Order! Order!" he shouted, "there's a priest in the house."

The crowd fell silent. Father Matthews addressed the dishevelled, embarrassed group. He asked sternly: "Are you not ashamed of yourselves, causing further distress to a family in mourning? Poor Brendan upstairs has hardly even begun his journey through Purgatory. Show some respect for him and his family. You are all behaving like a bunch of Protestants." Peace thus restored, the priest, with Frank and Mrs. McCrory, retired to the kitchen.

Immediately O'Neill raced across and grabbed McCabe, pinning him against the wall. "Right sunshine," he demanded, "now apologise for insulting my wife and also calling her ugly." McCabe retaliated with a powerful right swing to O'Neill's face and drew blood. The truce was over and the row resumed in even greater intensity – with male and female joining in. A few musicians in true Titanic spirit bravely played away, dodging flying missiles, in a futile attempt to create a more peaceful diversion.

Suddenly, a piercing noise sounded through the disturbance. Eddie had found an old referee's whistle, and was standing on a table with a hurley stick in his other hand. His threatening posture could not be ignored. Silence reigned once more. "Enough's enough!" he thundered. "This behaviour is outrageous. Poor Brendan is hardly cold yet, but you've paid no attention to Frank, or even to Father Matthews. You can carry on, but at your peril. The boys in the club not far from here owe me a favour. It's amazing what those guys can do with hurley sticks – and I'll be helping them. You've got to be sensible. Enjoy the rest of the evening peacefully, it's your choice, or else." Eddie's impassioned, threatening speech had immediate impact. Noisy normality was restored, and tidying up began. Remorse and apologies were evident all around the room.

O'Neill – now subdued – had released McCabe and was pumping his hand vigorously. "I'm sorry mate," he said. "Maybe I misunderstood you earlier about my wife. But do you really believe she is ugly?" McCabe replied, "Actually it was my wife, not me, who said it, and she's probably right. But my wife is no oil painting either, they've both seen too many birthdays. We men are different in growing older. We keep our good looks much longer. We have stronger genes, and more D.N.A. cells. Anyhow, forget about the women, let's get another beer before those drunks clean the bar out."

The party was quickly in full swing once again and the well-stocked utility room attracted thirsty good-natured activity. Patrick drained his last Guinness, and then exclaimed: "Good heavens! It's 3.45 am. Brian, we have had enough for one night. Let's head home. We have a busy day tomorrow." Eddie met them at the door. "You can't leave yet, boys, it's still early and more supper is on the way. Stay for a few drinks at least."

"Sorry," responded Patrick firmly, "we must go. It's been a pleasure meeting you. Could you organise a lift home for us?"

"I'll drive you home," came a slurred voice from a slumped body under a table. It was the banjo player in a drunken stupor. "As soon as I have another little drink for the road." The offer was wisely ignored. The two men finally departed, after a ritual of lingering farewells and the promise, "We'll see you at the funeral on Friday." Someone had thrust a packed supermarket bag into Brian's grasp as they staggered into the deserted street. He said appreciatively, "Boy that was some party. We even got a free carry-out of Guinness and sandwiches!" Patrick was still sober enough to remind him, "Remember, it's the same routine for us tomorrow. We'll have a well earned lie-in, then we'll go to the bookies and the pub around 2 o'clock. It will be your turn to get a paper, and be careful to buy *The News Letter* this time. We'll find out if there are any prominent Protestants who have died on the Shankill Road, and we'll invite ourselves to the wake for free food and drink, and a bit of craic. However you'll have to be more careful with any jokes you make next time. Anything about the Pope will be OK but give the Orange Order and Ian Paisley a miss, or you'll get us both knee-capped! And we can't afford that. These free 'wakes' are much too good to be true!"

MICHELLE McEVOY

"Goodbye Jade"

The clouded moon illuminates Jade's face as she walks through the gorse at the bottom of her garden and onwards through the green grass of the field beyond. The breeze lifts her white cotton dress and the wind is teasing her legs. It is bliss – nature is being kind to her tonight. She is not scared, yet part of her feels she should be. But she knows *she* is watching from up above, the spirit that watches over her and protects her, just like her Tarot cards told her.

As she enters the forest, she touches an ancient oak tree and its solid mass of rough bark is a comforting reality in her midnight reverie. To think she has walked into the forest at this hour! She carries on, deep into its sodden heart, the scent of the trees filling her head with satisfying dreams. She imagines she may walk into a trap, fall thousands of feet into an abyss below, even into the burning embers of hell maybe. The earth will open its lustful mouth and take her. She is a mere speck on the planet's clean surface. Why should she be spared? She tries to relax now, as she lies down and gazes at the moon and stars. She closes her heavy eyes and gives in to sleep. The wolves won't attack her tonight.

"Sleep, sleep, sleep, my darling child, feel the grass caress your bare arms. Feel the heat of the earth below you, all its layers there to support you, even the volcanic centre. Uncurl your pain and bury it - no, cast it into the waterfall and watch it drift away. Let it go, for you don't need it, you need tomorrow and lightness and love and solitude. You will learn how to live and laugh lying on this verdant bed. Let the magic carpet of this life sweep you away."

Jade opens her eyes and realises she is no longer lying on the ground. She is with *her*; they are somehow light and free, and this angelic force has brought Jade to an unimaginably lush landscape. The trees are dripping with life, and the grass seems to dance in delight under her feet.

"How did we get here?" Jade asks in amazement.

"My dear, we flew here together, don't you remember?"

Jade looks at her, and moves to touch her, but she is just out of reach. "I remember closing my eyes and feeling sleepy."

"You didn't fall asleep" she says, "You came here with me."

"Yes, but how did we get here?" Jade asks again.

"You know how we got here Jade," she says, this time more firmly. And then Jade remembers. It must have been just after she had fallen asleep. She had looked up and there she was, her beautiful eyes gazing at her. Her slim hand was outstretched towards Jade's and she didn't hesitate in taking it. Her white dress had floated around her once again as they ascended through the higher branches of the forest's majestic trees. Now Jade looks at her spirit in realisation, and she responds silently with a soft smile.

For a while all is quiet as Jade wonders what will happen next. "How did you know I was there?" she asks.

"You called me," the spirit said. "Don't you remember knowing that I was there when you came into the forest?" And of course Jade did know she was there, like the soft presence that filled her soul when she was alone in quiet places. "So what do you want to do now you are here?" she asks.

Jade looks around at the others, all sitting quietly, perhaps meditating or praying. They didn't seem to be doing anything much.

"Yes but what do *you* want to do?" she asks again this time more persistently. Jade realises she has read her mind and knows her thoughts already.

"I want to see him," she says firmly.

"I understand," says the spirit.

He walks towards her, just like she remembers him, with the soft smile which showed no teeth. "Hello pet," he says, "Whose girl are you?"

"Daddy's," Jade replies, without hesitation. She is a seven-year-old again.

"Are you OK?" he asks meaningfully.

"I don't know Daddy, I am lonely sometimes."

"Everyone is" he says gently. "You must learn to embrace it and not to reject it". He talks to her for a little while, and all the time she looks at him and feels her burden slowly start to lighten. Her thoughts become clear, and her mind seems free. Then he stretches his hand towards her and, before she has any time to think, they are floating, flying, soaring through the warm humid night. He envelopes her in his arms and protects her then, as they fly through putrid septic air. Now they land back in the forest, in the same spot where she fell asleep. "Goodbye Jade," he says. "Remember I am always here for you. Go home to your world, open your arms and your heart to your husband Will, and your family, that is your piece of heaven." And then, with a final peaceful smile and wave, he is gone.

Slowly, Jade's pain, for so long an unwelcome solace in her heart, begins to leave her, and she imagines it as wisps of smoke disappearing into the darkened sky and beyond. Her father, dead by his own hand, loved her and always would. She knew that now – there was no need to question it. She opens her eyes and realises that her back and legs are damp from the dew. Sunlight streams through the tall branches of the trees. She smiles as she remembers the kindness of the spirit, and the sensation of being above the trees, above the earth. Jade wonders then if perhaps she hasn't moved from this spot, all night asleep in the forest. Was it a dream? She isn't sure, but knows that something in her has changed.

She gets up and, straightening her white dress, she begins the long walk home. Moving purposefully now, she realises Will must be wondering where she is, and hopes that the baby is OK. She turns her key in the front door of their little cottage and climbs the stairs. There they are, both sleeping soundly. She unbuttons her dress and slips into bed beside them. Will's skin is soft and relaxed from sleep. The baby inhales and exhales her innocent child-breath. It feels good to be home. As she starts to drift into sleep she smiles to herself and starts to dream of an unimaginably lush landscape far, far, away.

The Butterfly Sisters

The old brown gate creaked loudly as the three sets of hands pushed it open. The girls slowly stepped through, into the space beyond. Giggling, they held hands as they felt the damp grass beneath their bare toes. Beyond the gate was a beautiful garden full of huge plants in every colour imaginable – yellow, red, pink, orange, blue, purple, white. The colours were so bright they had to squint. The grass was dark green, darker than any they'd seen before – could it be real? Their eyes opened in wonder as they looked around, and above, to the clear blue sky overhead.

The sun shone brightly and Nicola was glad she had sun cream in her rucksack. She told Donna and Zara to stop, while she gently rubbed the cream onto their warm faces.

"OK now, let's go," she said.

"Where to?" said the others.

"Let's just go," she said impatiently.

Suddenly, a little man appeared beside them. He was smaller than Zara.

"Who are you?" asked Zara.

"Sssh," said the others.

"My name is Orlo and I'm here to guide you on your journey through this secret garden," said the man.

They dared to look at his face, and saw that his eyes were the brightest blue they had ever seen. He wore a dark purple cloak, and, like them, no shoes. They clung tightly to each other as they looked at his hands and saw that his nails were long and gnarled, but clean. He had kind hands. Nicola whispered to her sisters, "I think we can trust him."

The old man started to walk quickly, saying, "Come with me." Zara had to run to keep up with him. They reached a small red wooden gate hidden among a cluster of trees. The trees had very thick trunks and pink leaves. They had never seen a tree with pink leaves before. Beyond this gate was a landscape so beautiful that it made them gasp.

"Welcome to my home," said Orlo.

Zara started to giggle, but her older sisters told her to keep quiet. A beautiful old woman dressed in a flowing yellow dress approached them.

"Do you know who I am?" she said.

They looked around for Orlo, but he was gone. They were speechless, shaking their heads in wonder. The lady's face was wrinkled, yet, like Orlo, her eyes were sparkling and she somehow looked young.

"I am a fairy," she said. "I'm here to look after you. Now, quickly, climb onto this carpet."

They all turned around and saw a brightly-coloured carpet floating at the height of Zara's waist. They found themselves climbing onto the carpet and sat, cross-legged, holding hands.

"Off we go," exclaimed the old lady.

Suddenly they were flying through the air, with the wind blowing their hair back; the feeling was wonderful. All too quickly, they were back on the ground and this time the grass was pink. They could hardly believe their eyes; it felt very strange to be walking on a pink lawn. They looked at each other and started to laugh; their eyes were shining with excitement.

"My name is Cherry. You are in the Land of Wishes. Here, all your dreams will come true. Come with me," said the old lady.

They started to follow her along a pathway to a strange brown house. When they looked closely they realised the house was made of chocolate. Donna broke off a piece of the front door handle and ate it.

"This tastes just like *Aero*, only better," she said.

Nicola and Zara couldn't resist, and went to the windows to break off pieces of the handles. It was the best chocolate they'd ever eaten.

"Come, come," said Cherry with a smile.

Inside the house, they saw three sparking crystal balls on a table in the centre of a room that was painted the colour of mandarin oranges.

"Put your hands on the crystals," said Cherry.

They did as they were told, and suddenly they realised that they were wearing ice skates. Following Cherry into an adjoining room, they found that they were skating behind her. Donna had been a little afraid of skating every since she'd fallen on an ice rink the year before, but she was moving like an angel. There, in front of them, was a beautiful ice-rink, full of children, just like them, skating around in wonderful fairytale dresses. Looking at each other, they saw that they were also wearing beautiful dressed covered in multi-coloured sparkling sequins. They found themselves dancing to Zara's favourite song, "Filthy Gorgeous" by The Scissor Sisters. They danced and danced, until they were dizzy.

There were pink velvet sofas around the edge of the ice-rink, and the other children were starting to fall asleep on them. Nicola led her sisters to three sofas arranged in a u-shape. They lay down and began to talk about their adventure. Soon they could not keep their eyes open, and fell fast asleep. They all dreamed of fairies dancing on a beautiful lake covered in ice, on a moonlit night.

In what seemed like only seconds later, they found themselves waking up in their own beds at home. They got up slowly, stretching.

"I had a funny dream last night," said Zara.

"So did I," said Donna, looking puzzled.

"Me too," said Nicola.

They all looked at each other and laughed nervously.

One week passed and it was Saturday night. As usual, the girls were curled up on the sofa eating ice cream and watching TV, waiting for their favourite programme *Dancing on Ice.* After the introductory music ended the presenter, James came onto the screen.

"Welcome Ladies and Gentlemen, Boys and Girls. Tonight is a very special night! Tonight is 'Kids Dance on Ice'," he announced.

Nicola, Donna and Zara watched, captivated, as child after child took to the ice. Soon there was a commercial break and, afterwards, James made a special announcement:

"Now we have three special girls competing tonight; please welcome 'The Butterfly Sisters'," he said.

The camera followed the girls moving around the rink. Their dance was very fast, unusual and stunning. They looked familiar. What was it about them? When they had finished, the audience clapped and clapped – it had been a spectacular dance.

Soon it was time for the winners to be announced. Runner up was 'The Buttercup Fairy', a lovely seven-year-old girl who screamed when her name was announced, and cried when she was presented with the trophy. Second place went to 'The Tree-Top Boy'. He too was thrilled with his prize. Everyone held their breath, in anticipation of hearing who had won First Prize.

The presenter didn't keep them waiting long, saying: "I am absolutely delighted to tell you that tonight's winners are 'The Butterfly Sisters'." By this time, the girls' ice cream had melted. They watched, speechless, as the prize was presented to the three girls on TV by a beautiful old woman dressed in a flowing yellow dress. There was still something very familiar about 'The Butterfly Sisters'.

The old woman said, "My name is Cherry, and I am really honoured to present First Prize to 'The Butterfly Sisters', three very special girls, better known to their family and friends as Nicola, Donna and Zara. Congratulations! Your dream has come true!"

Who Holds Frankie Now?

Little Frankie was so-called for his resemblance to Frankenstein – his head just seemed too large in relation to his body. According to the scant records, he was seven years old, but he only looked like a child of three, malnutrition and neglect having taken its toll. Every vein in his shorn head was visible through his paper-thin skin. His head had been shaved to stave off the lice, rampant in this orphanage deep in the cold heart of Romanian countryside. I first encountered him, crazed in his cot with his sad brown eyes and teeth protruding at all angles in a wild smile. Constantin (his real name) had been abandoned by apparently uncaring parents – who knows what their story was?

The first time I picked Frankie up he clung to my neck. I had to worry about his tiny nails piercing my skin. We were told to be careful about that, due to the possibility of AIDS. His little body was hard and tense. Still wearing a nappy, Frankie had never been cared for so he lacked control of his bodily functions. His skin and bones were usually encased in the simple cotton-striped trousers worn by most of the boys, along with whatever battered T-shirt could be found in the orphanage.

One day, shortly after my arrival, I picked him up with the intention of taking him outside to play. As I moved outside the door he squinted in the bright sun and immediately froze in fright. He clasped himself to me, legs wrapped around my waist, hands clinging to my neck, and obviously pleading for me not to put him down. Frankie couldn't or wouldn't talk. Each time I tried to release him, his legs just buckled and he sat on the ground. I muttered soothing sounds in his bony face and kissed him. "It's OK Frankie, I promise I won't let you go." He didn't relax his Vulcan grip until we were back in the safety of the yellow 'pre-fab' that was his home. I put him in his cot where he seemed to feel safe, and he resumed that crazed walk up and down from one end to the other.

At night, we would leave the kids with the Romanian carers. Weather-beaten women, with large families of their own to look after, they came in from work in the fields with their husbands, to work in the orphanage with the unwanted. Showing no mercy for handicap, there wasn't much love for their little captives. That was *our* job – the volunteers from Ireland.

One day I came in quietly in the morning, and saw Frankie's face redden in pain. He had started to choke on something. One of the 'carers' raised her hand and, with a flash of long painted nails, forced his mouth open, extracting the life-threatening object from his throat. He screamed in pain as she turned away from him, and I was aghast that she didn't even look back as she walked away. I ran across the room and picked him up, soothing his cries by stroking his skeletal back. Eventually he calmed down though no doubt his quiet throat was on fire. He sadly couldn't tell me.

Each day I continued to try to take him outside, for he really needed the vitamin D from the warm sun. For weeks he couldn't relax. I started to take him over to the relative quiet of the orphanage fountain with its one sad trickle of water, its grandeur long-faded. There we would sit, and I would hold and caress him, and sometimes manage to persuade him to leave my knee and sit on the ground. What had happened to Frankie that made him so afraid of the outdoors?

One day I turned away from him for an instant, and when I looked back he had stood up and was literally dancing with the delight of actually being on his feet. I dared not breathe, and just watched him smile at himself, a wee man, arms flailing. This continued, over the next couple of weeks. With a little caress and loving attention, he would just dance around aimlessly.

All too soon it was time for me to return to my comfortable lifestyle in Ireland to continue my university studies, opportunities that Frankie would never have.

I wonder if anyone bothers to touch Frankie now.

ANNE-MARIE FITZPATRICK

The Day I Met Bill Clinton

Another boring day ahead – dishes in the sink from last night's dinner, floors to be hovered and washing to be done. Sure I'll get it started after Brunch. There must be something more exciting to do in middle-age. So I decide to sit and watch the news on television. Gosh! I didn't realise one of the men I admire most in the world was in Belfast, but there, being interviewed, was Ex-President Bill Clinton. He had just arrived from Dublin where he was signing copies of his autobiography. Surely there must be a book signing in Belfast as well.

It was now 2pm, so I promptly rang Eason's Bookshop in Belfast. The girl told me he hadn't arrived yet but there were so many people had gathered, that she did not think he would have time to sign all of the books. Determined not to miss out on meeting Mr Clinton again as I had done on previous visits, I ran to the bathroom, had a quick shower, dressed, then drove to Belfast, parked car in Castle Court Shopping Centre and promptly made my way round to Eason's on Donegall Place. As I neared the shop, I could see flashes of camera lights and televisions camera beyond the vast crowd. I pushed my way through, but alas the staff were just closing the doors and Mr Clinton was being ushered to the back of shop, escorted speedily to a waiting car which roared off, followed by convoy of bodyguards, police escorts, jeeps and motorcycles. Drat, I'd missed him again.

Little did I realise that my adventure was about to begin. As the crowd dispersed chatting to each other, lots of people had autographed books while others had photographs. I found myself walking through the back streets of Belfast towards the Europa Hotel, where Mr Clinton was interviewed earlier while the sound of sirens faded into distance. Surely this was where he was staying. Once more I was literally minutes too late to meet my hero, who had just sprinted from his car, door still ajar, through the swing doors of the hotel. I was still determined as I got so near this time but I realized he would be leaving some time soon, as someone mentioned he had an appointment in Enniskillen the next day.

His wife, Hillary, had already left as she was speaking later that evening at the University of Ulster at Coleraine, explained a lady standing outside the hotel with her teenage son. The lady was holding an Eason's bag which contained Bill Clinton's book, including his coveted autograph. During our conversation she explained how they were lucky enough to meet him at the signing, after queuing from early morning then receiving a ticket to go in to meet him . . . Seemingly, Mr Clinton had stood at a podium, shook hands with each person and signed their books as they drifted by. They had travelled by bus from Omagh at 6am for this privilege, also intending to shop in Belfast for college clothes for her son Jason, who had accompanied her on the trip. No shopping was done, as it had started to rain. I convinced them we should try to get into the hotel and maybe see the Ex-President as her son, an autograph collector tried in vain to get his little book signed; but only autobiographies of Bill Clinton were being given this much-sought signature.

Smiling sweetly to the police at the door, and squeezing past a convoy of cars waiting to take off at high speed, to our amazement they let us in to the foyer of the hotel. Jason the teenager, whom I had just met with his mum, had a camera with him. By this time my adrenalin was jumping at the thought that my dream could still come true. This young man kindly told me that if we met Bill Clinton and he could get a photograph he would send me a copy. I promptly gave my address with his mum's blessing, still doubting it would happen.

Standing in the foyer beside the elevator that we hoped he would use, we were joined by another lady who arrived from Bangor. Even as we stood chatting, the excitement built up. We befriended bodyguards who informed us that Mr Clinton would leave in an hour. One hour turned to two, three and, even four hours later, with excuses every hour as to why there were delays. The lift was stopped and guests advised to use other elevators. Some people didn't even know Bill Clinton was in the hotel. Finally the elevator which was halted at floor ten, started to move slowly down to the ground floor. Security people scattered to different areas, police to waiting cars, massive jeeps and motorcycles outside the front doors with their engines revving as the impending getaway neared.

The doors slowly opened and there stood the great man himself. Tall, handsome and charismatic, just as I had imagined, a smiling

Bill Clinton strolled towards us. I then had the pleasure of shaking the hand of one of the most powerful men to have governed America – Mr Bill Clinton. He signed his autograph twice for me (just in case Jason couldn't get one). Jason got a photograph from behind his head, then suggested I try to move down the by-now formed queue. To my amazement once more Bill Clinton stopped beside me. I picked up the courage to ask if he would mind having a photograph taken with me. To my delight, he agreed as Jason nervously snapped away. The Ex-President smiled at me, stepped outside into his car and was whisked away at high speed, followed once more by the convoy of speeding vehicles.

My heart almost burst. I couldn't believe that my determination to realise my dream had made it come true. Two weeks later I became the proud owner of two photographs of myself with Bill Clinton, taken and sent by an angel in disguise, young Jason Marshal. It was a day to remember.

DAVID TIERNEY

Cow Karma

The most common thing people asked after my car accident on the way home from my meditation class was how I could fail to see a cow crossing the road. It seems ridiculous to try to think up excuses. One minute it was on the road, and the next it was trying to join me on the front seat of my car.

With a loud bang, the car took off in flight and a quiet panic arose inside me about what would happen next. I didn't have to wait long to find out. The air-bag popped, and a smoky cloud of chemicals descended in front of me. That was when I heard the celestial music. Well, maybe not quite celestial but quiet, relaxing and inspiring music, nevertheless. "What a clever invention," I said to myself. "This must be an airbag that plays music as you depart this world." Unfortunately, the thought had more to do with bumping my head on the roof than reality.

My car eventually stopped, and realising I wasn't badly hurt but stuck in the twisted wreckage of my car, I shouted for help. Through my cracked wing-mirror, I could see the cow corpse on the road. There was someone prodding it violently, and I heard a voice say, "It's definitely dead you know!" Briefly annoyed that the cow was getting more attention than me in my time of need, I shouted again. The 'cow-prodder' came over and helped me out, through the window of the car.

A helpful bystander said to take the ear-tag number of the cow, as farmers have been known to cut off that part of the animal's anatomy to avoid being traced and therefore to avoid paying insurance. The vision of cutting off a bloody ear caused me to spray him with the regurgitated contents of my stomach – which were the remains of vegetarian curry I had eaten earlier. He seemed remarkably calm. He said, "Don't worry about that. The insurance will pay my cleaning bill."

Let me try to explain the remorse I felt in killing a cow. I know that cows are slaughtered for meat all the time. I was a vegetarian Buddhist with strong ethical opinions on the sanctity of any life form. I may admit to having the odd bacon sandwich when I think that no one is looking and yes, I wear dead cow on my feet in the form of leather. Let me tell you about a holiday I had recently taken in Thailand to give you some idea of my outlook on life. My room was invaded by hundreds of 'creepy-crawlies'. I carried them outside, carefully, one by one. It took me hours. Unfortunately, the Buddhist Thai maid did come along and spray them into oblivion with the strongest chemicals she had. But that is not the point. I really am a sensitive, caring kind of guy.

Back at the scene of the crash, the police arrived. I should have known what direction the evening was going to take when one of them asked if I was all right. "Of course I'm not all right," I hissed at him and followed this with a string of curses. I told the policeman, "I have just hit a cow head on, bumped my head, wrecked my car, met the world expert on insurance claims, and threw up over him."

This cursing surprised me, as I had last used such strong language when I was eight years old and the beating I received from my father on that occasion meant that it had quickly disappeared form my vocabulary. It was a Sunday school prize-giving day, and the teachers had always shown a lack of originality in their choice of gift. "Not another bloody jig-saw!" I exclaimed to an open-mouthed congregation.

Both policemen ignored my outburst and the large one opened up his notebook and started to write. I suppose it's not politically correct to label someone as 'large' but that is all I can remember about him. The policeman suggested that I go to hospital, but I was not badly injured and frankly I would have preferred to go home. He opened the door of the police car by way of suggestion.

"If you don't mind me saying so," remarked our Helpful Bystander, "you'll get much more compensation if you wait for the ambulance – at least a thousand pounds more." I eyed him suspiciously and decided that even though what he said made perfect sense, I did mind *him* saying it. Ignoring him, I accepted the offer of a lift from the police, but not before telling them to make sure they had written down the ear-tag number of the cow. The parting shot from Helpful Bystander was to tell me to get all the pills I could from the hospital. "Even if you don't take them it will help your claim!" he shouted after me.

I never did find out from where Helpful Bystander materialised, but he seemed to know his stuff about cow collisions. Perhaps he was my guardian angel taking human form to help me through. (I knew all about these things having once attended a 'get to know your angel' course). Then again he could be a know-it-all idiot who took perverse happiness in other people's misfortune. Don't get me wrong. I am grateful that he pulled me from the car and his insurance advice was accurate and helpful but there was something about his sneering face which made me want to smack it – hard.

We were on our way to the hospital. The policeman, who had obviously been on a sensitivity course recently, joked how cow-jumping could be an Olympic sport, and how he had seen people squashed by smaller animals than a cow. This led to an impromptu quiz amongst the policemen as to what was the smallest animal that could kill you. "This must be Cow Karma," one of the policemen said. "We are always killing them for food, and then a suicidal one runs in front of your car to make a point!"

The "Cow Karma" comment worried me more than they realised. Let's just say that spiritual enlightenment is one of my things, and apparently the more enlightened you are the less likely you would have to wait until another life to reap the rewards of your actions. I had killed a cow. I smelled trouble ahead.

The hospital was uneventful enough. I waited around, and was given some x-rays and painkillers. The only misunderstanding came when they asked me what kind of car I drove and I answered "Friesian" instead of Ford. I was still confused by the accident. Nevertheless, remembering the advice of Helpful Bystander, I held my head a lot, and took all the medication offered. I was clearly starting to think about compensation.

As the news about the cow-killing spread among my concerned friends and family, I began to receive texts on my mobile phone. "There are easier ways to fill your freezer," claimed one, and another asked, "What did the poor cow ever do to you?" Not one of them enquired how *I* was. I had visions of the gable of my house being painted with the words "COW-KILLER." People are like that. They love to rub your nose in your troubles. I do think though that the little memorial and flowers that later appeared at the spot where the cow died was perhaps going a step too far.

The policemen kindly offered to pick me up from the hospital and take me home. Complete with collar on neck I got into the car. It wasn't long before the night took a more sinister turn. Over the police radio I could hear the sense of urgency in the operator's voice. "There's been a shooting. Get there quickly." The Karma Cop turned to me and said,

"Sorry sir, we have to go to this one right now." Before I knew it he put his foot down hard on the accelerator. I felt every bump in the road reverberate through me as the car picked up speed.

As we arrived at the scene I could see nothing unusual, apart from someone on the outside of the car pointing a gun to the window saying they were going to kill me. "Oh no, this is really my night to die!" I thought despondently. "The cow didn't get me and now you are going to. Goodbye cruel world. Enlightened? I must be on a par with the Dalai Lama. First, I was hit by a cow and now I'm really going to die." My yoga training had not prepared me for this. I began to chant, but it was nothing like what I had learned to memorise during my mantra evening. I suppose the words "Don't lose control of your bladder," doesn't really count as a positive affirmation, but that's what I needed at the time.

In a split second, and with a rugby tackle that any of the Irish team would have been proud of, the gun-pointer was wrestled to the ground as the weapon bounced off the car and slipped on to the road. He was quickly handcuffed and led away, but not before I shouted instructions that on no account should he be put in the back of the car with me. The police called for another car, and we resumed our journey to my home.

The berserk gunman turned out to be an off-duty policeman whose gun had been removed from him weeks earlier because he was exhibiting bizarre behaviour. Trying to kill innocent members of the public *is* pretty bizarre. "He did threaten his wife and kids earlier on," the large policeman said as if this was going to make me feel any better. "We thought his mood had improved and he got the gun back."

I guess guns and problems don't mix – a bit like cows and cars. He then tried to lighten the mood by saying it would really make my evening if I got home and found my house had been burgled. Some things have a habit of happening in threes. It took all my years of quiet contemplation at the Buddhist retreats, combined with the stark reality of a possible night in the cells for assaulting a police officer, to stop me from punching him.

When we reached my house, everything seemed fine. Neither the TV nor the computer was missing. No one had a daubed "Cow killer" on the wall. No posse of cows were waiting for me, determined to wreak their revenge. All was as quiet as an empty cowshed.

The biggest change in me since that night is that I do not believe in Karma any more. I no longer shake my chakras. I find meditation mediocre. There is not an angel card in sight. I swat flies. My chant is now a rant. I eat big juicy steaks, rare. Maybe I am just storing up trouble for myself but what do I care? I have faced Cow Karma and survived.

Death by Instalments

You are lying on the operating table gasping for breath and a single tear is flowing down the grey contours of your face. The doctors have asked me in to say my goodbyes. You are frightened, and for a moment I want to take away your pain and make it all better but only for a moment. In reality I am looking forward to the finality and relief of your death. Then and only then will I be able to get on with living my life.

The pain of your death will be as nothing compared to the pain in keeping you alive because in reality I have watched you die a hundred times and I have already grieved. For me tears no longer come, only resentment and sadness. You will be free from suffering soon, and I will carry this with me for the rest of my life. It is New Year's Eve and some of the staff are talking about the parties they will attend later on. My wife is dying and you are talking about celebrating. Life must go on. You look at me again and I kiss you on the cheek and grab your clammy hand. It's not long now.

Suddenly I think that perhaps I have got this wrong. Keep her alive. Doctors have all the answers don't they? They study for years. I'm sure they can do something. This is not death Hollywood style. This is messy – complete with breathing equipment, the smell of death and fear. I scream at them "do something" but they avert my gaze, calmly stating that they are doing all that they can. This is not the quiet dignified death I imagined. This is you starting to fight to stay alive but why now?

The first time I grieved for you was your falling down stage. Friends were over for dinner and you fell off the chair hitting your head on the wall. Just before you were twisting the wine bottle as you poured it into the glass so that you would get very last drop out. "Cheer up," you said. "It's a party." You fell down a lot, and every time you fell I picked you up. Your body kept the score with a bruise or a missing tooth. Everyone noticed. Was it the drink or were you married to a wife beater? Lots of activity at the bed now as I am shunted out of the way.

Your eyes are closed, and for a moment I see your face as it was when we first met and your beautiful sparkling smile; but I look again and it is gone. Your face is twisted, and small noises rasp from your mouth. It contains an explosion of crooked and rotting teeth. I used to tenderly kiss that mouth. I move closer to listen. "Help me," you say. "I'm scared," you say. I touch your cold marble-like cheek and try to look concerned. For some reason I think of vomit. How many times did I see you with your head down the toilet bowl? How many times did I wake up during the night to the feel of urine-soaked sheets and mattress?

After every treatment programme it was always the same. "No more drink. I have changed. I do not need this any more. I want to change. I will not touch a drop." Days later the little signs would appear that you had started to drink again. You always prided yourself on your appearance, but now you did not care. You stayed in bed for days. "I'm sure a few glasses of wine won't hurt me," you'd say.

You lost your job. More time for drinking. I asked you why you drunk and you always had a range of ready-made excuses. You said I was a controlling prat, your mother beat you as a child, you were abused and previous partners beat you up. You started to get fits, but refused to take your medication. You were depressed and drank cocktails. I became your carer and not your lover. Don't get me wrong. I did not act the dutiful husband. I took sex from others when I got the opportunity. I wanted to leave, but stayed out of pity and the thought of what others might say.

I started to have vivid dreams. You were in a river and I was on the bank. Never a strong swimmer, you were struggling and I threw you a lifebuoy. You did not reach for it but continued struggling. I jumped in and you pushed me away. I shouted to save yourself and you ignored me. You started to float away, and I could only watch.

How many times have I begged you to choose life and only now are you starting to fight. "Let's take her to intensive care," I hear a nurse say. A knife twists in my stomach. So she is going to live. Typical. No quick exit for you. Improving. How much more? I am moved to a family room and suddenly notice the concerned looks of everyone around me. Perhaps they feel I am cold and heartless. Am I not behaving as a good husband should? Am I cold and indifferent? Where did all this compassion fatigue come from? Have the years of living this hell sucked it out of me?

I try to remember the good times, but all I can remember is pain, false hope and the verbal abuse. The smug-faced addiction counsellor said that she has to ask for help. At this point I had the urge to lean over and rip out his insides. You don't have to live it, watching someone die – this death in stages. I hear the sound of footsteps and I know that whoever they are they are heading this way. The door opens and I am told that she is dead. It is said in such a matter-of-fact way that it catches me by surprise. The doctor is young and before long is bounding out of the door.

I start to cry and feel pain like I have never felt before. Noises that I have never heard spew out from the inside. I lie on the floor and shake. I could not save her and now she is dead. I wanted her dead and I did not want her dead. I am scared to let it out, as I feel it will engulf me and everyone in the room. My chest heaves up and down and I struggle for breath. Short, sharp pants. The noises keep coming.

Suddenly I realise that before I was grieving for myself and now I am grieving for her. A sense of relief floods over me. I am not the monster that I imagine myself to be. I feel real love. I did what I could and I am not to blame for her death. The warm memories flood back. That excitement in the pit of my stomach when I first saw you. The way you threw back your head when you laughed that revealed the softness of your neck. The knowing glances when in the company of others and the touches and whispers of reassurance. The talking and caressing hours into night. These are the memories that I will try to carry with me as I face the months ahead and as I begin to live my 'life, by instalments'.

Teaching a Lesson

The small boy stood at the top of the class shivering with embarrassment. "Capital letters do not come out of lucky bags you know," the teacher howled. "Sort out your punctuation. My job is to teach the illiterate peasants of the world like you how to write, and it is a lost cause."

He paced up and down as he addressed the class, occasionally repositioning his glasses on his nose as if to add a bit more gravitas. From time to time he would move toward the culprit, giving his victim's ear a hard tug. He continued his rant: "As an accomplished writer I am wasted at this school trying to teach the basics to thick hillbillies like you. You are hopeless. Let's hope that whatever job you end up doing that writing is not involved."

It was all becoming a little too much and at this point I felt a warm wet trickle run down my leg. It wasn't long before the others saw it as well, and a crescendo of howls filled the room. "He's pissed himself," someone shouted. At this I began to cry but there was nowhere to go. It was clear that the first time my school teacher saw me it was not love at first sight. He did treat the rest of the class badly but he reserved his sadistic streak for me. I was from one of the roughest areas of the neighbourhood. As far as he was concerned there was no hope for anyone from there.

My attempts at essay writing were read out to the class in sarcastic tones. In an attempt to impress, I would put in as many big words as I could, and was accused of getting above myself. "He's swallowed the dictionary," crowed the teacher. "Try to stay at your own level .You had a cat and it sat on a mat, ha ha!!"
He turned to the class and pointed to me, stating that I was a classic example of the perils of in-breeding. Every day we were told that when his books started selling he would retire from teaching.

My bladder control and writing ability improved. It was when I started university I heard that he was now making enough from his writing to give up teaching and his particular speciality were historical writings about the local area. It was 10 years before our paths crossed again, rather unexpectedly. I was working for an American publisher and we had acquired an Irish publisher in a merger. Looking through the contracted authors I saw the name of my former teacher. His picture in the profile started to bring it all back.

My contacts told me that he had taken to drink and that he regularly boasted that is was only a matter of time before his talent was discovered and he could move onwards and upwards. He had also lost a significant amount of money through gambling and was considering returning to teaching.

The authors knew there would be cuts, but there was excitement as well as an Irish author had recently had great success in the US – culminating in an appearance on the Oprah show. After the merger, one of the first e-mails I had from my boss said that we had to trim the Irish operation and lose some of the underperformers. It was time for me to have a little fun with my former tormentor. The beauty of e-mail is that you do have to use your own name. He had no idea who I was.

Dear Sir,
We have not met but as Chief Executive of Purpose Books we are reviewing our contracts and at first glance I find your writing a little stuffy. Your use of English is of a style more suited to the classroom than the literary world – an ex-teacher perhaps! A change is required. While I'm at it, there is only some of much of this historical dribble we can take before losing the will to live.
Regards
John Murray

Dear Mr Murray,
I am sorry you do not like my writing style. I was a teacher and perhaps this has had an undue influence. I would be interested in writing about topics of interest on rural affairs.
I am willing to consider any changes you wish to make.
Regards
Michael

Dear Michael,
I see from your photograph on our publicity material that you have a beard. The public do not react well to people with beards – they

feel they are hiding something – please shave it off if you wish to continue working with us.

As for rural topics, how about something on plant breeding? I believe that's something of interest to the locals.

You did say you would consider any changes.

Regards

John Murray

Dear Mr Murray

While shaving of my beard is a little extreme – my wife likes it. If it enables me to continue working with your organisation I will comply.

I did not think that anything on breeding plants would sell, but I will send you an outline for consideration.

Regards

Michael

Dear Michael

Yes great! The history of plant breeding – how it developed, why people do it, what are the problems for plants.

I hear you are thinking of going back to teaching. I trust this is only rumour, as we need our writers to be full-time. While I am sure your teaching struck a chord with your former pupils, it is nothing I'm sure to the intense feelings your work conjures up in your readers.

Please e-mail me a photograph to prove you have got rid of the beard.

Regards

John Murray

Dear Mr Murray

I had heard you Americans were thorough. As you can see from the attached photograph I have shaved the beard off.

What do you think of the outline?

Regards

Michael

Dear Michael,

Seeing you without the beard the only way you could tap the American market is by getting plastic surgery, paid for by the organisation, of course. Would this be an option? Also it helps if your wife and kids look good. Do they? Or have they inherited your ugly gene! If they have, there is nothing we can do about that (the offer of plastic surgery is for you alone).

I am only joking of course. You will have to get used to my American sense of humour. You do *look better without the beard though.*

Your outline sucks. You should write about what you know. You were a teacher. What about something on the old teaching methods. I hear they were strict, but effective!

Just a small point. We like our authors to be teetotal, and I have heard on the grapevine you are fond of a drink.

Regards

John Murray

Dear Mr Murray,

I do not drink alcohol.

I attach an outline on old-style teaching methods in Irish schools.

I am sure I will become used to your frank method of communication.

Yours

Michael

Dear Michael

As your last email was a little curt, I fear I have offended you. Remember Oprah and the big bucks. It will be worth it in the end.

Your outline is a little tame. We need some tension. As a teacher didn't you feel like whacking the little buggers? I hear most of them were a little on the intellectually-challenged side. A friend of mine went to one of your Irish schools and one of his classmates actually wet himself!

It's not that I don't trust you, but we will need medical evidence that you are off the juice.

Regards

John Murray

Dear Mr Murray
It is true I used to have a little problem with the drink, but that is all in the past. I attach a sample chapter on teaching methods in Irish schools.
Regards
Michael

Dear Michael
To paraphrase a well known critic – this is not a work to be cast aside lightly but hurled with great force. It really is bad.
One small point. Your punctuation is a little unusual. Capital letters do not come from lucky bags you know!
Forget the medical evidence proving you are off the drink. No one who is drunk could write that badly.
That's only my opinion though, and Oprah likes it and is keen to see it in print.
Regards
John Murray

Dear Mr Murray,
Oprah Winfrey likes my work? Does this mean that we start discussing the contract?
Regards
Michael

Dear Michael
I'm afraid not. Oprah works in my local dry cleaners' and only reads books with pictures in them. She does like plants though.
Your contract is not being renewed. I was at the receiving end of your teaching methods a long time ago. While on the surface this was bad – you were a sadistic sod. It was good because it made me work even harder, so on balance I do not hold a grudge, and years of therapy have helped. I will deduct the cost of this from anything you are owed (only joking).
You are being dropped because you are a very poor writer who

does not sell, rather than as a poor teacher who made my life hell!
Regards
Paul Williams

PS: Do not go back to teaching, as then I really will have to call
Childline.
PPS: Apologies about the beard.

The Joyrider

Six months before my father died, it was clear that his driving days were coming to an end. Reports came from various sources that he was driving dangerously fast, or pulling out in front of other cars. The Parkinson's Disease that was breaking down his body was beginning to have a dramatic effect. This was due to tremors, but also because he was less mentally alert and was becoming increasingly confused behind the wheel.

The fact that he was able to continue driving for so long into his illness was because my mother had become his navigator. It was she who would keep him right by watching for traffic or telling him to slow down. Her methods were often drastic. My father was profoundly deaf, and she would have to shout the instructions to him. Before she got into the car with him she would check that his hearing aid was switched on, as he had a habit of turning it off when her nagging became too much.

She had a few methods to make him take notice like pulling the handbrake or elbowing him violently. He would remind my mother of her only attempt at learning to drive which ended up with the car a mangled wreck. Then a few things happened which demonstrated action needed to be taken. While driving out on his own he was spotted attempting to go round a roundabout the wrong way. He also was at the receiving end of some road rage after he turned out in front of someone. The aggrieved driver followed him home and started to shout at him on the driveway. Completely unaware, Dad asked my mother if the man was trying to sell them something.

I got all sorts of advice from people about how to deal with the situation. He obviously had to stop driving but advice like hide the keys, sell the car or confront him did not take into account how much being able to drive meant to my Dad. For him driving was independence. It was being able to go where he wanted without depending on others. The car was also an opportunity to help those without transport. He would take neighbours shopping or would give them lifts to church, chapel or hospital appointments.

Talking it through with him, I said that we would both meet the doctor and see what his advice would be. The doctor told him that as a temporary measure he should rest from driving, but we both knew that he would not be behind the wheel again. Despite his penchant for speed he had always been a careful driver. "It is the others on the road you need to watch," he would say. "Look ahead and anticipate".

Leaving the Doctor's surgery that day, he handed me the keys. He was a quiet dignified man and not prone to emotion but I could see he was hurting. This was another sign that his life was changing. He stared at the floor. I was feeling for him, and my face crumpled with sadness and, as if he noticed this, he stated that driving was getting stressful for him anyway and that he was trying to look at the positives – namely no digs in the ribs from my mum or a constant commentary on his driving skills.

Over the next few weeks his mental alertness continued to decline. When I visited him one day he pleaded with me to take him to the garage to get his car battery charged. Ten minutes later he emerged from the shed covered in red paint. At first I panicked, as I thought he was bleeding but he explained he was marking his battery as he did not want the garage giving him back a dud one. He continued to wash and polish the car. I explained to him that I did not need to treat him like a child and that I would leave the keys with him, but on no account was he to drive. My mum reported that he would regularly start the car and rev it up.

It was two days later that I got a frantic call from my mum. "Your dad's disappeared and so has the car," she said. I rushed down, and just 200 metres from their house a small crowd had gathered. I jumped out and saw my dad driving round and round a piece of waste ground at high speed. The car window was open, and I could see pure joy on his face. The looks on the faces of the spectators was more like terror as they scattered in different directions. He yelled like a kid, as he did lap after lap. This was the father I did not think I would ever see again, energy and enthusiasm radiating from every pore. This was no longer an eighty-year-old Parkinson's sufferer – this was a man in the prime of his life.

"Stop the car and put the keys down Dad!" I shouted. The car ground to a halt and the crowd breathed a collective sigh of relief. "Is that man a joy rider?" asked one young girl. "Yes," said her mother. "Probably one of the oldest you'll ever come across." Dad emerged from the car and shuffled towards me. "I just wanted to see if I could still do it," he said. "I have now officially retired from driving." A broad grin spread across his face.

Two months later he was dead, and instead of remembering his last days in hospital I recall the look on his face that day. I remember his sense of humour, his courage, his support for others and his wish to live life on his own terms. His was indeed a life well-lived.

STELLA MITCHELL

A Good Shepherd

Mary Ann watched from the back porch as her son ran across the yard and shut the double gates so, so, quietly, but the old dog was not outfoxed. Shep leapt over the wall and landed at Matthew's feet. The dog danced round and round the young master, maintaining strong and pleading eye contact as if asking, "Take me with you . . . Take me with you." Matthew about to say, "Stay," instead heard himself give in. "Come on then Shep, our last walk together. Let's go and see some wee black-faced sheep and we'll see Eileen too."

Time to say goodbye, he thought, and suddenly he felt a choking in his throat. Tears ran down his cheeks and he ran up the lane with the dog trotting along beside him. Today the old dog was subdued. Could it be that he felt the sadness that pervaded the whole farm and all about the place. New Zealand was a long way away, but Mary Ann never doubted the wisdom in sending her dearest child so far. He would greatly benefit from the wealth of knowledge he would gain from cousin Robert George on his large sheep spread. Robert George had written plainly that, if Matthew was the boy his mother said he was, then the farm and all on it would be his when he was done.

There was another reason why this good Irish woman was able to part with her son; this was the year 1912 and there were rumours of war in Europe. Mary Ann knew that Matthew would be one of the first to join up because she had heard him and some of his friends talk about it as though it would be some great adventure. Then there was Eileen . . . Mary Ann could see that they were no longer children playing together and she welcomed Matthew's departure to bring the developing romance to an end.

Matthew hurried on up the lane leading to the mountain where Eileen would be waiting. He stopped only a few minutes to pick some primroses and a couple of wild violets. Today he was more aware than ever of the beauty of the land and the mountains and the sea where he had grown up. Again the tears flowed, "Lord, stop me crying, please," he said. There was Eileen at the mountain gate. "I could hardly wait for you, how long have we got?"

"A couple of hours, the sisters have been baking all week for the tea and my mother will want me to be on time."

Arms around each other they made up the steep incline to the sheep pad that would take them round to their favourite place, a grassy bank with a great big boulder of Mourne granite on which to rest their backs. "My Da says that the real reason you are going is to get away from me because I'm a Catholic." Eileen's directness took Matthew unawares. Then, good fellow that he was, he answered as truthfully as he could. "I think he is right in a way, but you know my Mother's cousin wants me to go there because he is getting on and he has a big spread of sheep and wants me to work with him because I am a good sheep man."

Eileen snuggled into his shoulder. He gave her the small and rather warm posy of wild flowers, and he kissed her cheek. Matthew's feelings for Eileen had grown stronger and stronger this last while but Eileen was younger than him and he felt a duty to look after her and not take advantage of her feelings for him. Her father had made it more than clear to him that he was to respect Eileen. They sat with their backs against the big rock nicely warmed by the sun, and they spoke only now and then. Eileen talked a bit about her plans to go to the city to train to be a nurse, but Matthew was too heart sore for words.

The plaintive cry of ewes so recently deprived of their lambs filled the air, for it was late spring and the cruel separation had taken place. Separation everywhere! No more would he and Shep work the sheep together. No man would shepherd his wee black-faced ewes better than he. In the worst of winters Matthew and Shep had dug them out of snow drifts up here – Shep was the one to nose them out and start the digging, with his two front paws sending the snow flying. Never again would this man and this dog work in hard winters up here, nor would he feel the heavy burden of the ewe across his shoulders as he carried her to a safe place. He smiled as he thought of some of the places the lambs had got to; up on ledges and down between boulders. Many a time he had feared that he would be the one in need of rescue. He looked down to the shore and laughed out loud at the picture he recalled of himself and some young neighbouring farmers adrift on the water in their home-made crafts. Lucky they were not to have been drowned.

Eileen held his hand tightly and clung to him when he turned to her saying, "Don't wait for me, love, for I will be a long time away. Enjoy your life and be a nurse and be happy. Write to me sometimes and tell me the news." He hugged her tight as they stood up, and then they clambered down the side of the hill and he walked with her to near her home.

It was a bitter-sweet family meal that evening – one of the wee sisters was in floods of tears and ate nothing, for she clearly loved this good brother who was leaving them. The next morning, early, the men who worked on the farm took breakfast with Matthew. The old shepherd who had taught him much of what he knew stood at the steps of the pony and trap, turning his cap round and round in his shaking hands. "God Bless you Matthew, you good boy, come back if you can," he said. Mary Ann herself always drove the pony and trap and now she invited only the old shepherd to accompany her and Matthew to the train. The old man could scarcely contain his great happiness to be going these last few miles with his good boy.

To Matthew's great surprise Eileen, on a very old bicycle, also went part of the way. When Mary Ann got as far as the chapel she stopped the pony and told Matthew to get down and bid Eileen goodbye. The young people hugged each other for a moment and then Mary Ann gently suggested to Eileen that she might go into the chapel and say a prayer for Matthew's safe journey.

In 1912 it took a long time to get to New Zealand but for Matthew it was all new and such a great adventure. Matthew showed his worth from the first day he started to work with Robert George, who liked his young distant cousin. He remembered the boy's mother as a fine person and now he found her son Matthew to be a splendid young man.

The feared troubles in Europe rumbled on, and by 1914 the clouds grew very black. War was declared and Matthew felt the great pull of home. He was resolved to go back to his homeland to see his Mother and family and Eileen who had faithfully kept in touch. Despite his cousin's wise counsel Matthew returned to Ulster with the clear intention of joining his former classmates and neighbours in whatever army regiment was meant for them.

So it was, that in 1916 these young men of Ulster found themselves in Northern France and marching towards the Somme. Matthew was amongst them in the Medical corps; his two winters of evening classes taking First Aid qualified him as a stretcher-bearer. Every man was a volunteer, and they marched towards the River Somme with a buoyancy of steps. Many of them sang, and some played mouth organs. "Home for Christmas," they called to each other but the great adventure in France was soon to be carnage as the campaign continued.

Early in the morning Matthew had some breakfast in the trench with the other soldiers nearby. Then it was over the parapets and soon they were falling . . . even as they were going over. Within the first five minutes thousands were cut down by the endless hail of enemy fire. Waves of men went over and those that weren't killed were in a terrible state. Back and forward Matthew and the other stretcher-bearers went – they were brave, and countless young men were brought back from 'No Man's Land'.

When there was no stretcher-bearer left alive to work with Matthew, he threw the stretcher aside and carried the wounded men back across his shoulders as he had so often done with the sheep on a wild winter's day at home up on the mountain. Many of the young men cried either in agony or complete mind-breaking astonishment at the great noise, the thunder of the guns, the whine of shells and the mud and the rain and sheer fear. The fear was not acknowledged, but the exhaustion and white faces were there to be seen.

The more comrades Matthew brought back the more he began to feel they were indeed his wee black-faced sheep. "There, there, I've got you," he'd say to the young groaning in pain. He spotted a badly-injured young fellow well out in No Man's Land, and resolved to carry him back regardless of the risk. He was so young and so frightened that Matthew took him up in his arms and sang to him as he made for the trench. As he handed him over to a strong pair of hands he said, "Take good care of this wee lamb." Then, as he turned to go back again into the noise and mud of No Man's Land he heard a whizzing sound just before it struck him in the chest.

This Good Shepherd's work was done. As the light faded from his dying eyes the nurse leaned forward and stroked his face, "That's my good son, I'm well pleased with you." He heard her fine contralto voice sing just a line "The Lord Bless Thee and Keep Thee." Then, Eileen ran towards him laughing, and holding out the posy. "What kept you so long?" she said, her eyes smiling with her undying love for him.

It's All Over

The lamp threw a soft circle of light onto the highly polished table and across the heads of the two children. The girl was reading and the boy was drawing a horse. Save for the laborious ticking of the ancient clock and an occasional crackle from the hearth, there was no sound in the room. The mother of the children lay resting on a sofa drawn up to the fire. Her hands were quite empty; now and then she would bring them up and gently stroke her pregnant body. The flames from the fire threw shadows across her face, a face that was all eyes; they stared through the flames and beyond. A quiet sigh escaped her breast.

The girl looked up, and her eyes rested on the face of the clock. It was half past eight. Outside the wind howled and screeched round the corner of the house, and the rain fell in torrents from a black starless sky. The child lowered her head again to the book, but the big frightened eyes saw no words. She was listening. Her brother looked up and they exchanged startled glances, for the heavy knocker was being pounded on the door. All three jumped up, startled by the very thing that they had been waiting for.

Two men came in. The girl's quick eyes took in their unaccustomed dark suits and black coats. She hated them for their premature correctness; she hated them for what they had come to say.

"It's all over," the older one said. He sat down on the sofa and took the woman's hand. She let out a strangled cry and whimpered.

The girl's eyes grew bigger and her face turned white; she swayed on her thin little legs. The other man bent to put his arms about her, but she turned from him to her brother. The boy moved towards his sister and took her hand. Tears ran down his chubby cheeks and he looked from his mother to the man beside her in questioning bewilderment.

The younger of the two men took the boy in his arms, and beckoning the girl to follow, he took them to their beds. Ignoring her own bed the girl got in beside her brother. The man was quietly talking to the boy, but the girl ignored him and all that he was saying. Silently she waited for him to leave them in peace, but he stayed. Sitting down on the side of the bed he went on talking:

"Your father is happy now," he said, "For he is with God in heaven."

The girl's loathing for the man grew in intensity. Why, she wondered, could he not just say that their father was dead? Because, he *was* dead. Why did he say that their father was happy when she knew that he was not? He would not be happy to be dead; he would be cold and lonely but she could not lie beside him and warm him as she had done when he was sick. She closed her eyes and pretended to be asleep, and then at last the man turned the wick of the lamp down and tiptoed out of the room.

From outside the door she could hear muffled voices. Then her mother entered the room, and quietly took something from the big cupboard. It was her father's best suit. For a moment the mother stood there, a pair of shoes in her hand and a look of anguished indecision on her face; then she quietly placed them back in the cupboard. The boy had turned to face the wall and was sleeping soundly; his sister lay flat on her back. Outside the tempest still raged and her eyes grew heavy and she slept.

Before her, in her dream, a man rose up out of the hazy mist and hovered – just beyond her reach. He was dressed all in black, but he wore no shoes. Although his back was turned towards her she recognised him and a smile broke across her face. With outstretched hands she called to him but he made no reply – neither did he turn round. She tried to run towards him, but her feet were heavy and as she stretched out again and again so he moved away, and away, and away. Despite her pitiful pleading he was gone – away – back into the mist from whence he came. In the bed the little figure shuddered and tears ran down the cheeks of the sleeping child.

PHILIP GORMLEY

A Secular Priest

Patrick Joseph Gormley was born on 28 October 1916, the third child of Mr and Mrs Philip Gormley, shopkeepers of Carnanbane, Claudy, Co. Londonderry. He was educated firstly at Kilgort Primary School, Park, Co. Londonderry and then at St Columb's College, Londonderry, which had been founded to act as the Derry (Roman Catholic) Diocesan Seminary.

He was such a distinguished pupil of St Columb's that he formed part of that élite group admitted as clerical students to St Patrick's College, Maynooth, Ireland's National Seminary in 1934. In those days, admission to that venerated institution was confined strictly to the most distinguished pupils of 'the College' and of its Irish contemporaries, North and South. Young Patrick Gormley held a County Council University Scholarship, as did many of his equally distinguished contemporaries there. The high tone of his class was further elevated by the arrival in Maynooth of the students from the Irish College in Salamanca, who were forced to relocate to Ireland due to World War Two.

Patrick Joseph obtained an N.U.I. degree in Celtic Studies before his ordination as a Deacon in 1940. He became a member of the biggest and most distinguished class in the history of St Patrick's College, which included amongst others a future Cardinal Cahal B. Daly.

However, a dispute with his Bishop, the autocratic Dr Neil Farren, meant that the Reverend Patrick Joseph Gormley left Maynooth just before his ordination to the priesthood, compelled to pursue his 'secular vows'. Those 'vows' proved to be nothing of not multi-faceted in the case of Paddy, as he was now normally called. Thus he started out as a shop assistant and 'van-man', taking his father's mobile shop all around the foothills of the Sperrins. In effect, this meant dealing with his father's poor but severely demanding clientele in that epoch of wartime rationing. Doubtless it came as a 'quare gunk' (or a profound culture shock) after all those years in celibate academia. But he adapted more than well to the new challenges, thanks partly to his warm and generous personality and also to his well-developed sense of dry humour which remained distinguished features of the man all his life.

His application of his 'secular vows' (Maynooth's term for the activities of its non-ordained alumni), was a very fine realisation of those high Christian principles which had been taught to him both at home and later on by his various distinguished mentors- and not least his neighbours in Carnanbane and the surrounding area.

As a young 'pillar of the community', he was elected a County Councillor in the late 1940s, and eventually he became the Londonderry County Council's longest-serving member. When he was married in December 1949, this was another case of his pursuing 'secular vows'. His wife Moira McGurk, from Gulladuff in South Derry, had three brothers who were priests and one sister was a nun. Without doubt, her Catholic credentials were more than acceptable even to such a distinguished Maynooth man as my father!

In due course, "Father" Patrick Joseph Gormley became a father in a different sense and he and his wife had three children. Paddy worked as a merchant, selling those excellent potatoes of north Co. Londonderry and beyond to England, all over Europe and beyond – including Cyprus, the Canaries, and Egypt. His further involvement in public life increased when was elected as Nationalist M.P. for Mid-Londonderry at Stormont in late 1953. He was a committed believer in the development of people through the practise of Parliamentary democracy, and he remained faithful to that ideal all his life.

Gormley's Sinn Fein opponent in 1953 dismissed him as a 'mere Redmondite'. Though unintentional, it was a splendid compliment, as the Sinn Feiner knew nothing of the huge personal sacrifices made by the Redmond family as MPs for Wexford down the years. And it turned out to be an unintentional prophecy about Gormley's further career in public life. The pressures upon my father's time in the 1950s meant that I was reared in part by an extended network of "mothers and fathers" between our home and 'the shop', as we ever called it. Our housemaid 'Mena' Gormley was our 'second Mammy', and the atmosphere in the shop was ever homely and friendly, which was a reflection of the easy-going nature of our paternalistic "boss."

When we moved out of the shop in late 1959, the other 'parents' faded away, but the bonds between my father and I grew much, much stronger. I was an impassioned follower of politics, on his account, and our bonds were strengthened by a common fascination with both billiards and football. Thus we would start our evenings at home with a game of billiards, and our weekends were occupied with such serious matters as following St Columb's College's football teams in all of their competitions. That same period saw us both bonding further around the great days of Derry City football club in the Irish League.

Such matters aside, my father's life in practical terms was a beautiful articulation of his Maynooth secular vows, as he brought a robustly practical Christianity to bear on all his work, both in public and in business. He was respected by all his colleagues in both Stormont and in the County Council because of his intelligence, integrity and liberal and generous personality. Lord Brookeborough, the Unionist Prime Minister of Northern Ireland, put it nicely, when he said "What a pity Paddy Gormley wasn't a Protestant!" Had he been such, he would indeed have been a Minister.

A neighbour in Ballyrory paid my father an intriguing compliment when he refused to act as Unionist election agent against him, and said "I would rather cut off my right hand than stand as agent against Paddy Gormley." In Stormont, his friendships spanned the entire political spectrum, from its Prime Ministers down – indeed, he held, and was held by, his Protestant brothers in more esteem than his 'rougher' Catholic colleagues. In a talk to Maynooth students in the '60s, he said that 'every constituency gets the MP it deserves'. Asked by the lamented late President of Maynooth (and later Cardinal) Tom O'Fiaich what he thought of Eddie Richardson, the-then Nationalist MP for South Armagh (who was something of a 'character'), he said, "He is just the case I had in mind!" During his hospital stay in the 1960s, he was visited by Prime Minister Captain Terence O Neill of whom he remained ever a friend and (reciprocated) admirer.

As an M.P. my father was ever consistently a real Parliamentarian and a true Nationalist, in that grand tradition of Daniel O'Connell, the Redmonds and his political mentor Cahir Healy. He saw his Roman Catholic brethren start at long last to mature politically in the 1960s, and to see Stormont start to develop its first-ever realistic Parliamentary Opposition. His work included, *inter alia*, seeking to help bring the professionalism of new graduates in politics into Stormont, not the least of the new entrants being the very able Austin Currie. He also set about encouraging his Catholic brethren to enter into a mature 'Social

Contract' with the Northern Ireland State. His 1965 Stormont election acceptance speech sets out a vision of a properly professional and mature Catholic political party in NI from which all of Ireland could still benefit today. Within the Londonderry County Council under the leadership of my father and his colleagues' (all of whom were wretchedly underpaid) there was seen a fine standard of efficiency and integrity, which was truly 'power-sharing' in effect.

In his other main activity as potato merchant, my father's work was also a practical application of his 'Catholicism in action'. He helped financially innumerable small farmers grow potatoes under contract by taking care of their seed and fertiliser bills. The money from his potato purchases was an major economic input to countless homes around the Sperrins – and one man at least turned up at his funeral to express in practical terms his thanks for my father's charity.

This phase of his life (and mine) came to a tragic end in 1965, when he was injured in a serious car accident. He managed to make a significant physical recovery accident, but a mixture of domestic, practical (and Catholic political) factors saw him cease to be an MP at the same time as he had to relinquish his potato business. It was a traumatic period, but he managed to develop a constructive retirement marked by his care for a blind wife of formidably strong personality. He also looked after their home, and developed a magnificent library, and all this was achieved with a dry Ulster sense of humour.

My father and I escaped in July every year on an eclectic annual tour of Ireland – which was also a patriotic study of Ireland's hills, beaches, boarding houses and bars, not to mention the 'Ecclesiastical Circuit' of his fellow-alumni from Maynooth (all of whom were Canons by that stage!) Their fraternal bonds remained amazingly strong after 40 or 50 years.

It was only during those pilgrimages that I learnt fully about as that distinguished 'Maynooth Phase' of my father's life. Indeed, this modesty was a typical Gormley family characteristic. His public life was painfully short, but he displayed that same fine Christianity as he did on his private life later on. I am profoundly grateful for all the graces received from Daddy down the years, and I remain ever consoled by the certainty that his soul now enjoys its proper place 'at God's right hand'.

FIONNULA McGOWAN

The Cure

"Put yourself into God's hands," the old priest said as he took Ellie's hand and looked deeply into her eyes. Her expression was desolate as she sat in her wheelchair, her right arm and leg useless and heavy, her speech, once vibrant and witty, silent now these past two years.

Annie had taken her Aunt Ellie to see Father Thornton, who was renowned for his healing ministry and having a cure. She wasn't convinced herself, but hoped that Ellie would derive some sense of inner healing, even if she wasn't cured of her stroke. She watched now as a silent tear spilled down her aunt's pale cheek and felt her own emotions threaten to overwhelm her. The old priest had said no more and, after a few moments of quiet prayer, he guided them to the door.

On the journey home, Ellie gestured for Annie to open the window. She seemed faint and began to gasp for breath at an alarming rate. Annie stopped the car and ran to open the passenger door to give her some air. She reached for a bottle of water in her bag and, with difficulty, managed to get her to drink a little, which seemed to revive her. The effort of this, however, had exhausted her, and by the time Annie got her home, Ellie was only semiconscious.

Within hours of calling the doctor, Ellie now lay in the darkened bedroom gravely ill. Annie was musing about the words of the old priest and, despite being a sceptic, could not help but wonder at the coincidence. "This was her cure," she thought. Ellie was being healed through death. Doctor Phillips, the family doctor, came into the room just then. "How do you think she is, Doctor?" Annie said in a low voice as she noticed her mother, now dozing by the bedside.

"She's very ill, Annie. How long has it been since her last stroke?"

"Two years this March, Doctor, She's never spoken a word since, as you know."

"Tragic," he said. "It was an unusually dense stroke but I'm afraid this second one has been catastrophic. It's highly unlikely that she will regain consciousness. You know Annie, I'm glad for Ellie, she's endured a long sentence locked in this silent world." The Doctor dropped his voice. "Your mother refuses to let her go to hospital, but I shouldn't think it will be too long in any case."

As the doctor left the room, Annie gently shook her mother. She looked down at the soft, downy cheek and felt a sudden surge of love for her. "You go and lie down, Mum, and I'll stay here. I'll call you if anything happens. Go on, you're exhausted. I'll wait with Ellie." Annie took up the vigil by the bedside, gently mopping Ellie's brow.

The day was drawing to a close and Annie moved to the window to draw the curtains. As she was returning to the bedside, her foot caught an upturned edge of the carpet and she fell heavily against the side of the wardrobe. She rose quickly, rubbing her shoulder and glancing over at the bed. However, Ellie remained in a deep sleep.

The force of the fall had opened the door of the wardrobe and an old shoebox had been dislodged from the inside shelf. As Annie lifted it to put it back, she noticed inside a small bundle of cream envelopes tied with a blue ribbon. Curious, Annie lifted them up and examined the writing on the front – *Miss Eleanor Mitchell,* the line read in fine, spidery writing. "The full title," thought Annie smiling. Ellie had been christened Eleanor but for as long as Annie remembered she had been called Ellie, despite her protestations that *Eleanor* was much more fitting for such a lady as herself.

Annie was about to put the letters back when the postmark caught her eye; the letters had been sent from Dublin. She glanced at Ellie just as she gave an audible sigh and shifted slightly in the bed. Annie untied the little bundle and cautiously drew out the first envelope. She turned it over in her hand, examining the front and then the reverse, where she noticed the letters *m* and *e* intertwined.

Intrigued, Annie slowly drew the letter from the envelope. Feeling a little guilty, she glanced up once more at Ellie. She nearly fell off the seat. Her aunt's eyes were wide open and staring straight at her. Shocked, Annie dropped the bundle of envelopes to the floor. Just as suddenly, Ellie's eyes closed and Annie put her hand to her head, her heart hammering in her chest. After composing herself, she bent down gingerly to retrieve the letters, then moved to the other side of the bed, having first ensured Ellie was comfortable. "Do you mind if I read one, Ellie?" she whispered to her aunt. She hoped that Ellie had heard, even if she couldn't answer.

Eleanor, the letter began,
I couldn't believe it when I saw you on the train today. It has to be destiny of some sort. We have seen each other only four times, yet each time I am completely overwhelmed by you. I hope it is the same for you. You didn't see me at first today and I had the chance to watch as you took your seat and made yourself comfortable for the journey. Eleanor, (I could write your name a thousand times) you are so lovely. You shook your glorious auburn hair, shiny, like a chestnut fresh from its case when you removed your hat and I just thought how perfect you are, so very beautiful. The silliest of things: you began to take off your gloves. I watched as you looked out the window with a little secret smile on your face and I hoped you were thinking of me...

Annie looked up from the letter, feeling her face redden. She felt a rush of guilt and hastily replaced the letter in the envelope, carefully tying the bundle again. She moved back to the other side of the bed, facing Ellie in wonderment.

Ellie had worked in the Civil Service for thirty years before she had been cut down by a stroke at the premature age of fifty. Her work took her to many parts of the country, mainly to Dublin, but also visiting farmlands and custom offices. She was only four foot eleven and expertly compact, having tiny, proportionate hands and feet, a delicate little nose, small ears and lovely, oval light-brown eyes. She was a talented artist with an extraordinary soprano voice reminiscent of Deanna Durban. She had never married. Lawrence, her first love, had died tragically in a road traffic accident on his way to collect her from work. Ellie had never lost her sense of guilt and for many years didn't go out of her house at all.

Her health had always been precarious, having suffered rheumatic fever as a child. She loved travel and it was on a long flight to America that the first signs of heart trouble were detected, leading to open-heart surgery. The operation had been successful, but in the ensuing weeks, Ellie had become withdrawn and depressed. Annie tried to recall the sequence of events.

Ellie had lived with them for as long as Annie could remember. She recalled the summer following the surgery, Ellie returning to work, and attributed this to the positive change in her aunt's mood. She travelled back and forth to Dublin during these months and, each time, she was like a new person on her return. It was strange how clearly the pictures of those last nine months of Ellie's *normal* life now seemed. Small memory windows emerged: Ellie singing in front of the large, bevelled hall mirror as she combed through her lovely hair; Ellie laughing with Annie's mother, head thrown back at some shared observation; Ellie lying on the carpet in front of the fire, looking so young as, lost in her thoughts, she stared deep into the flames, her cheeks rosed by the heat.

Annie looked tenderly at her beloved aunt and silently thanked God for having given Ellie someone special with whom to share her great capacity for love. It had been the following March when, without any warning, Ellie had been struck down with a blood clot to her brain, which had resulted in the stroke. Stroke, Annie mused, such a gentle word for such a devastating condition.

Annie looked at Ellie's face again. She seemed more relaxed; her breathing was easy and her eyes closed now in peaceful sleep. Unable to hold back her curiosity any longer, Annie took another letter from the bundle and began to read:

Eleanor,

Such a beautiful place you took me on my recent journey North. I hadn't been to this part of Inishowen before. Walking up the bramble lane to the cottage was idyllic. The sweet fragrance of the wild woodbine above the burn is still with me. Do you remember you plucked a little sprig and held it against your brow? I watched as you carried it for a while, pointing out the road through the hills to the mysterious valley of the Holy Well and Mass Rock. As we rounded the bend to the 'Bushes', the old thatched cottage of your childhood summers, you dropped the flower and I lifted it into my pocket. It is a little piece of you, my love, that I carry everywhere. Thank you for the gift of sharing your childhood home with me. The spring by the mountain heather and the view of that beautiful Lake of Shadows, Lough Swilly, was breathtaking. I will wear the memory of that place against my heart in the cold winter nights.

I'm sitting here this evening at my desk. Lena is in one of her black moods. This morning I found her crying at the bottom of the stairs where she'd fallen. Her nightdress was ripped and stained from a small, bloody gash on her head. The whiskey glass had shattered beside her and she was scooping what was left of the drink into her hand, disregarding the broken slivers of glass. She flew into a rage when I suggested that we should get a doctor to look at her wound.

I finally persuaded her back to bed and washed and bandaged her head as best as I could. I can hear her now, pacing the floor above. She's restless and knows that there's no drink left in the house. It's going to be a long night.

But you, dear Eleanor, you, my love, how you sustain me in these times. As I write this, your beautiful spirit warms and restores me . . .

Annie looked up quickly as Ellie sighed audibly, but her aunt was sleeping – peacefully, it seemed. The third and fourth letters told more of the life of Ellie's friend. His name was Michael, she learned, and he was a senior civil servant, like Ellie. He had been married for twenty years and devoted to his wife, though she had long been a hopeless alcoholic. What struck her from his writing was his loyalty. He spoke of her with tolerance and great compassion. His sadness flowed through every line as he spoke of his love for Ellie.

Annie reached for the last letter and took it out. As she did, a smaller, brown envelope fell out of the main packaging. She left it aside as she began to read Michael's words:

Eleanor,

How I wish I had met you earlier, my darling Eleanor. It is so unfair to you that I can only offer you my love from a distance. When we are together, it is all I can do to restrain my physical need of you. I dare not cross the line; if I do I know there would be no stopping. I've got nothing to give, Eleanor. It's hopeless. I can't leave Lena, especially now she is to go into hospital tomorrow. The doctor says her brain has been affected; she becomes more violent by the day. Last night, she broke two windows at the bottom of the stairs with her fist. It's a miracle she didn't cut herself more seriously. I've taken your advice at last, Eleanor, and confided in my doctor. Lena needs more help than I can give her. I haven't been fair to her, trying to conceal things for so long. I should have sought help for her earlier. I will try to . . .

Annie was puzzled by the abrupt ending of the letter and realised he hadn't finished it. She turned it over, but the back was blank. She remembered the brown envelope then and picked it up, turning it over as she did. In large capitals, the word *BITCH* screamed at her. Almost simultaneously, Ellie's eyes flew open and Annie fell back in the chair. When she recovered from the shock, she leaned forward and whispered to Eleanor.

"Ellie," she said. "Ellie, you're awake. Are you OK?" Ellie's face was ghostly as she looked at Annie, then very deliberately looked down at the letter in Annie's hands. "What is it, Ellie? Will I open it?" Ellie nodded almost imperceptibly. The date was written at the top of the envelope, 23 March. Annie frowned; she struggled to capture a memory, one just beyond her reach. The twenty-third of March; why was that so familiar? She opened the letter and began to read, the opening lines startling her beyond belief:

You crafty little tramp! You didn't know I knew about you, did you? Well it's all over now. You see, he never was going to leave me for you. Did you really think he would, you stupid tramp? Oh, I knew all right, knew from the first day he met you. He was different when he came back. Tired, he'd said, when I asked him where he had been. He just said he was tired and went to bed. I knew he'd met someone, knew by the look on his face. I watched him after that. I saw him in his study, and a smile on his face as he would pretend to write reports, but I knew it was to you. He put me to bed tonight as usual and brought me up some tea, all sweetness and light. But he couldn't bluff me, not tonight, not after I heard him talking to the doctor, wanting to put me away. I knew his game. I crept down behind him to his study. He was writing, then leaned back on his chair as he took out something from his drawer. I waited to see and then he turned around and I could see that it was a flower of some sort. I nearly screamed when I saw him kiss it, then put it back in the drawer.

I stayed behind the door as he went out to the kitchen and went to the desk. I saw your name then, written on the envelope, but it was still open. I just caught the opening line before I heard him coming back. When I confronted him, he just stood looking at me, saying nothing. He tried to tell me I wasn't well! Me! Such a laugh! Tried to get me to go back to bed. I wasn't going to fall for that again. I ran to the desk and got out the precious flower and tore it in front of him. And still he stood there. Only when I promised that I would make sure that YOU, would suffer, did he say anything. He came towards me, telling me that I was wrong! But I ran past him, upstairs with the envelope. He came after me, but I was too quick. He'd nearly reached me at the top when he missed his footing and fell. Broke his neck. He never got to finish the letter, but I kept it and the envelope. He's DEAD. So now you can go to hell, TRAMP!

Annie dropped the letter in disbelief. She reached out to Ellie, wanting to lift her up and cradle her. She had been so maligned. Suddenly, she gasped in shock as realisation dawned. The date of the letter was 23 March. Ellie would have received the letter two days later, 25 March. The same day that Ellie took the stroke. Annie closed her eyes and could only imagine the devastating and terrible shock her aunt must have received. Pinned to the letter with a paper clip was an obituary notice:

Kavanagh, Michael, 55 years.

Suddenly. As the result of an accident at his home.
Dearly beloved husband of Lena.
Funeral procession will leave his home tomorrow 1 March to St Vincent's Church for Requiem Mass and immediately afterwards to the City Cemetery.
Loved and will be so sorely missed by his devoted and sorrowing wife.

Annie looked at Ellie, tears in her eyes. Ellie was animated now, and agitated. She gestured to Annie with tremendous determination. It was a familiar gesture, recognised by Annie over the past two years: Ellie wanted to write.

Annie held her breath as she watched the supreme effort made now by Eleanor. After what seemed an eternity, Annie took the page from her aunt. In shaky, almost indecipherable writing, Ellie had written the word *BURN*. "You want me to destroy the letters, Ellie?" Annie asked.

Ellie, exhausted by the monumental effort, nodded weakly, then gave a long sigh. At once, her breathing began to change. Her colour flushed, then paled again. Her head turned to the side. Ellie's eyes were open, but this time she looked beyond Annie towards the window. A deathly rattle sounded from her chest.

Annie stayed stock-still. She knew Ellie was dying. She watched, frozen, as her aunt lifted herself up in the bed, pointing towards a spot behind Annie with a radiant smile on her face. Just as gently as she had arisen, Ellie sank, as if in slow motion, back to the pillow and softly breathed her last. The peacefulness of her passing echoed the peace that now came upon Annie as she felt a great sense of being blessed by the witness of Ellie's death and the miracle of her cure.

There would be time enough to call her mother. She leaned over to kiss Ellie's brow, resting her cheek on her forehead. Her eye caught the fine gold chain with the delicate Claddagh lying on the now-still breast. Reaching over, Annie turned it round to see what she now knew she would see: the gold letters *m* and *e* intertwined within the heart.

A Social Service

Hannah Carton's first day at her new job was a catalogue of disasters. The bus, always fairly reliable, was running late. The new navy trouser-suit from the high street store, she discovered too late, had a button missing and one of the hemlines was drooping. As she fiddled with a pin at the bus stop, a lorry-driver took his bend too fast and skidded, spraying the waiting bus queue with a tidal wave of filthy water. Still, as she climbed the stairs to the Social Services building, Hannah was determined, despite her now less than satisfactory appearance, to create as good an impression as possible.

"Can you tell me where I can find Mr Paul Clarke?" Hannah asked, smiling at the blonde-haired receptionist, who was typing furiously, tongue protruding in serious concentration. Without looking up, the girl nodded her head in the direction of the door to her left. The title on the door read: *Miss Estelle Hogg – Senior Personal Assistant.* "Grand title!" thought Hannah, eyebrow raised as she knocked at the door.

"Come in!" an imperious voice commanded. "Hello," smiled Hannah, taking in at once a snapshot of a moon-round face with large bulbous eyes and what could only be described as 'old hair' – wiry and unruly, like too many perms gone wrong. "God forgive me," thought Hannah wickedly as her smile widened, "she's like a telly tubby having a bad hair day."

Hannah's smile vanished, however, as the woman before her stood up, her eyes cold. She didn't speak a word as she scrutinised Hannah from the bottom of her feet to the top of her head with overt disdain.

"You're the new social worker then?" She raised her eyebrows with distaste and once more her eyes travelled over Hannah, settling on the muddied trousers. "I hope you dress more like a professional befitting your title when you go out to the public."

Face burning, Hannah shot back, "I have an explanation, but obviously you have reached your own conclusion. Could you advise Mr Clarke that I'm here, please?" Hannah's tone matched that of the older woman. As Estelle's eyes narrowed dangerously, Hannah knew that the blades had been drawn. "Mr Clarke is at a meeting. He expected you at nine o'clock. Not one for giving a good impression, are you?" she said, again violating Hannah's attire with a scathing glance. "Please go outside and wait at reception until he is free," Estelle Hogg gestured dismissively.

Hannah could not believe the rudeness of the woman as she left the room. "Not off to a good start there. What a nasty woman! I know what her Christmas present's going to be: a year's subscription of 'Wella Hair' products." She briefly entertained the thought that she was being uncharitable before indulging her whim. "Bad hair day today, Miss Hogg, or is that every day?" The thought sustained her childishly until the appearance of her new boss Mr Clarke.

Paul Clarke was a tall balding man in his thirties. He had dark good looks, with an attractive Mitchumesque dimple and a hearty laugh. She liked him immediately. Paul took her hand in welcome and laughed as Hannah apologised for her late arrival and the cut of her clothes. "Life's never straightforward, Hannah. Never worry," he said, guiding her towards his office. As he came by Estelle's room, he opened the door, one hand on Hannah's elbow.

"Hold all the calls, Estelle; I'll be busy with Hannah for a little while. Have you been introduced to Estelle?" Paul looked over his shoulder at Hannah. "I don't know what I'd do without her. She keeps me so organised that I sometimes wonder if I'm needed at all."

"Oh, you're needed, Paul," Estelle laughed, head tilted coquettishly.

"Yes, we've met," nodded Hannah, amazed by the change in the older woman's demeanour.

"Oh, and by the way, Estelle, I'll need you to do Hannah's typing in the meantime, if you don't mind, that is. The other typists are very busy at present."

"Of course," smiled Estelle.

As Paul strode forward to his office, Hannah glanced quickly back at Estelle, who glared at her furiously. "What is her problem?" mused Hannah, "crush on the boss maybe," as she smiled sweetly back at Estelle.

"Come in, Hannah." Paul gestured for her to sit down. "I'm so happy to have you join the team; it's been a while since we've had any female colleagues. The last two ladies we had left within months of starting the job. No reflection on women, now," he added hastily, "just coincidence. But both cited stress for the departure. Now, I know you've had experience of the job through the voluntary sector, so I hope you'll go the distance. And don't forget that I'm always here if things get tough. You'll have a period of induction and then begin to pick up a caseload. Estelle has prioritised all the waiting list cases for me, so I'll ask her to give you a file to start you off, familiarise yourself a bit with the types of problems some of our clients are facing. Any questions?"

Hannah laughed easily. "Where do I start?" she asked. "Yeah, I suppose that was a bit of an onslaught," Paul laughed, as he sat back in his chair. Hannah smiled, displaying a row of even white teeth as she tumbled through a list of questions she wanted to ask. She had a natural grace about her, which was striking, and an eagerness in her voice which Paul found captivating, his thoughts momentarily eclipsing Hannah's words. "So young," he thought. "On the cusp of life. Was I ever like that? Was I ever so hungry for experience? So naïve, though, a bit of growing up to do."

"I'm sorry," said Hannah, "I'm going on a bit."

"Not at all, Hannah, it's good to hear some enthusiasm again. You'll find the work can sometimes be a little tough, but don't worry, you'll have plenty of support here. Come on, I'll show you to your new office."

Paul led Hannah through to the end of the corridor. The room held three desks and two filing cabinets. It was fairly basic until a newcomer came to the window. "That's amazing!" exclaimed Hannah. "What a view!" The window looked out at the swollen river, which spilled and bustled over the rocky underground steps. The hills behind were etched into the sky as though copper-fastened there by a celestial hand. "So beautiful," said Hannah. "I'll need to have my back to this if I'm going to get any work done at all."

Paul smiled. "I'll send Estelle in with a file for you now so you can make a start."

Hannah drew her hand across the desk and closed her eyes. She felt a frisson of excitement. A new start, a blank page of possibilities. She'd work hard; she'd make a difference... Her thoughts were suddenly shattered by the thump of a red-backed file on her desk. "The Stewart file, a difficult case," said Estelle, "but I'm sure you'll be fit for it," she added, her expression enigmatic and bland, only her eyes betraying a hint of . . . what . . . a warning . . . a threat?

As the weeks went by, Hannah found Paul to be a good mentor. She related well to her other male colleagues, who were always tearing in and out of the office. Passing ships in the night. Only at the close of each day did they have a little time to relax, and then, usually only to pool thoughts about the various crises of the day. Hannah always kept up her spirits, and her quirky sense of humour endeared her to the rest of the staff. No matter how hard she tried to have conversation with Estelle, however, she was met with monosyllabic responses, or snide remarks, until Hannah finally gave up. She noticed that Estelle was distinctly different around Paul and caught the older woman often blushing, and smiling at her boss as she meticulously organised his day.

It was a clear day in March when Hannah was called into Paul Clarke's office. "Lord, I hope it's nothing to do with that last housing report. I had to rush it through," she thought, unconsciously smoothing her skirt with her hands. Paul's door was closed, and she knocked before entering. "You were looking for me, Paul?" she asked, brushing her long auburn hair back from her face.

"Hannah, a second unsigned note has come into the office about the Stewart woman. It may well be malicious, but I would like it checked out today."

Hannah took the piece of folded foolscap paper and opened it .The words were again written with red pen and in block capitals:

WHEN ARE YOU PEOPLE GOING TO DO SOMETHING ABOUT THAT GIRL AND THOSE CHILDREN? SHE'S NOT FIT TO BE A MOTHER.

The name scrawled across the top was that of the young family Hannah had been allocated as her first case in this new office. Melanie Stewart was a young widow with two children: her husband, Andrew, had been tragically killed a few months earlier. The case was all the more tragic because Melanie's father-in-law, a widower – and a wealthy bank manager in the town – had disapproved of his only son's marriage. It was following a heated argument over Melanie that Andrew had stormed from his father's house into the path of a speeding lorry and been killed instantly. Hannah was reflecting on this as Paul cut in:

"Is this too much for you, Hannah? Estelle intimated to me that she thought the case might be too difficult for you; she seemed really concerned about the reports she's been typing for you and was worried that it might be too much. I've no problem re-allocating this, Hannah.

I'm very happy with your work to date. This is a complex case and I don't want to lose another good worker to stress."

"No, please," urged Hannah in a low voice. "Please, Paul, I can handle it. I know I can."

"Okay," sighed Paul, "but keep me informed. We'll be splashed all over the headlines if anything happens to those children."

Estelle again. Hannah gritted her teeth . . .

Hannah closed the door of the office behind her, unsettled by the serious allegations made against Mel Stewart, yet still trusting her instincts that these had to be unfounded. This was the second allegation of this type, and Mel had been devastated when Hannah had confronted her with the earlier one. "My God, Hannah! You don't think I would do that?" she had cried in a shocked voice. "I'm all my children have left." And she had slumped to the chair in tears. Hannah had been upset to see this girl in such a state and tried to reassure her.

As she stood at her desk now, she could feel the anger rising in her. The home was basic but clean, and Mel had created a warm environment for her little family, with some nice touches throughout. As for her father-in-law, Alexander Stewart, Hannah tried hard not to judge the man too harshly; after all he had lost his only son. How do you cope with that?

She had learned that Alexander had not attended the funeral, but had chillingly sent a letter to Melanie, offering her two thousand pounds to hand over the children to his care. "What kind of man is that?" Melanie had asked her. "What kind of man would want to take children from their mother?" She had spoken gently, more in disbelief than anger. When she refused, Alexander had ended all contact, and she had not heard from him since. What kind of grief drives that kind of hardness and bitterness? What kind of man would refuse to contribute to his sole living bloodline, two beautiful grandchildren? His daughter-in-law was scraping a living, in dire circumstances, and he remains distanced. More to be pitied, she thought. "Yes, more to be pitied," she now said out loud. She could feel Estelle's eyes on her as she walked from the office. On more than one occasion, she had caught the woman watching her from the window as she went out to do her work. Well, she hadn't time to worry about her today; she had more important matters at hand.

Hannah approached the house, hoping she would get Mel at home. Mel answered the door and with a wan smile invited Hannah into the house. She was paler than usual, Hannah thought, a little thinner. Hannah watched as the young girl moved across the room. She was twenty-four, only a year older than herself, but she seemed to have the weight of the world on her shoulders. Her fair hair was uncut and fell lank against her shoulders. "The Electric people wrote to me. If I don't pay the arrears, they're going to cut off the supply . . . and the rent is overdue." Her voice was a monotone.

"Let me see it," said Hannah. "Two hundred and thirty-six pounds! That's a lot, Mel. Are you sure that's right?"

"I wouldn't know," she said, shaking her head. "It's just another bill."

"Look, Mel, don't worry; we'll get them sorted. I'll go through the lot with you and we'll see what we can do."

Hannah was aware that she had to address the issue of the letter with Mel, but looking at the troubled face of the girl, she didn't know how to begin. She looked around the house, at the Spartan furniture and peeling walls. The two children were sleeping in the old-fashioned double pram by the radiator. Hannah tiptoed over and looked down into the flushed and chubby faces of the baby girls. "They are so beautiful, Mel. You've done a good job."

Mel's eyes filled up. Hannah reached over to pat the shoulder of the frail figure before her and with all her heart wished that she could take away some of the haunted pressure bearing down on this unhappy woman. "Mel, this is the last thing you need to hear, but I'm afraid that there's been another allegation." Hannah reached into her diary and brought out the letter, handing it to Mel.

Mel clutched her stomach as she read the words. "I can't . . . can't . . ." she began, her face crumpled with anguish. Then she laid down the note and walked over to her children. Whispering something to them beyond Hannah's hearing, she laid her hand on the pram.

"Mel, I know you're a good mother. Have you any idea who might be doing this?"

"It doesn't really matter, does it?" Mel sighed. "It's just more of the same."

"No, you're wrong, Mel, it does matter. Get angry! Come on, you need to fight this; you deserve better. Have you any problems with your neighbours?"

"I don't know," Melanie sighed, walking to the window. "I've never had many dealings with them. I keep myself to myself."

"Try not to worry, Mel. I know you're a good mother, and I have no trouble standing over that anywhere."

"Thanks, Hannah." Mel suddenly smiled. "Thanks for everything; you've been a good support to the children and me. You know what? It doesn't matter any more, we'll be fine. You're going off for your Easter holidays tomorrow?"

"Yes, tomorrow's my last day before the holiday," Hannah replied, puzzled but pleased at the change in the young woman's mood. "What about you, have you any plans?"

"Oh, me and the girls will have a lovely time here; I'll take them to the park."

"That's great, Mel. Good for you; don't let things get you down. It can all be sorted; you're doing great."

"Hannah, would you mind now . . . I'm a wee bit tired and would like to get a bit of rest before the children wake up."

Hannah nodded her head. "No problem, Mel. I'll call in tomorrow, and if you need me, just ring this number – it's the direct line into my office."

As she left the home, Hannah turned to wave to Mel, who had already closed the door. She suddenly felt strangely uneasy and furrowed her brow. "What's the matter?" she asked herself. "What is it?" Finding no answer, she shrugged it off and returned to her car to complete the rest of her morning visits.

She had intended to return to the office for lunch, but it was such a beautiful day, she thought she would go for a walk. The day was warm and full of spring; this was her favourite time of year. Hannah stopped the car just outside the town and got out, walking the short distance to the laneway. From there, she followed the path which led to the small river, breathing deeply the clearer air, and feeling some of the tension leave her body. She often came here during her lunch break. She strolled lazily, inhaling the heady scents of bramble and gorse. The morning's rain had cleared, leaving a glorious aftershock of sweetness in its wake.

Just as she approached the small car park in the clearing beside the riverbanks, she stopped suddenly. The carpark was usually empty at this time of day, so Hannah was surprised to see an expensive-looking dark-blue estate car. The driver, his back to her, was gesticulating to a lady passenger. Hannah couldn't quite see her face. She suddenly froze as she recognised the red Fiat Uno parked just behind. Just then, the driver's window glided down in one fluid motion. Instinctively, Hannah crouched down behind the back of the car.

"I'm doing my best," the distinctive voice of Estelle Hogg was lower now, and Hannah strained to listen. "These things take time. How do I know you'll keep your end of the bargain?" the voice asked urgently.

"I'll have the money in your account today, but I'm not happy this is taking so long. You told me that she would break, that you could get an order against her. She's not fit to be with my grandchildren."

"It's going the right way," Estelle's voice held an edge. "That new girl Carton has no experience. Lucky she came along at the right time, arrogant little madam, thinks she's doing a good job," she laughed mirthlessly.

"I'm not interested in your petty jealousies, Estelle. I know your style, don't forget. You're quite the vicious bitch when it comes to competition. Now, I want my grandchildren; you need the money. Simple business transaction; I expect you to deliver," the driver said shortly.

Hannah's heart was now thumping in her chest as she understood the implications of the conversation. She was about to turn and run when she heard Estelle's next chilling words.

"I gave Paul a third letter today, after Carton went out. It read: *Your daughter-in-law*

"Don't call her that!" the man interrupted angrily.

"Okay," hissed Estelle. "It said: *the mother was seen in the bar last night, drunk, and had left the children unattended.* Paul was really alarmed. Can't take a chance with children, that's what I told him. He told me he was going to alert the police; they'll probably pick up the children until an investigation can be made into the allegations. That's when you come in and offer to keep them until the dust blows over. The girl is fragile enough, according to Carton's reports, so it should be enough to send her over the edge. Then you're home and free."

All Hannah could think of now was how to get to the office before Estelle. She backed away quickly into the laneway. Suddenly, she stopped. Something Estelle had said. "Who will believe this?" she thought. "Should I confront them?" Before she could do anything, she heard car doors slam and the vehicles rev up as they exited the car park.

She stood where she was, stunned by what she had heard, she had to go and tell Paul Clarke immediately. Something else began to tug at her thoughts. Melanie . . . she had to get to Melanie, "it should be enough to send her over the edge" . . . the way she had said goodbye, the brightness of her eyes.

Hannah ran back to her car and drove straight to Melanie's home. As she came to the door, her heart was racing. The curtains were drawn. She knocked at the door, but no one answered. Hannah ran to the back of the house and was met with a similar scene. She tried to see through the curtains, pulled tight at the back of the house, to no avail. Knocking at the windows, now frantic, Hannah began to shout, "Mel, Mel, are you there? Let me in!"

Hannah banged at the back door again, then pushed at it. The lock had been faulty and, after another push, came away quite easily. The stillness of the house was the first thing she noticed. Hannah called out as she went into the hall. "Mel, where are you?"

Hannah moved quickly now. "She must be out," she thought. "She must be out; there's nobody here." In the kitchen, she looked around. Two unwashed cups lay on the worktop, beside the kettle. The box containing the baby's feed lay open, powdered milk scattered around. A smaller brown pill bottle lay on its side, the grainy residue of its contents coating a nearby spoon. Hannah grabbed the bottle; the yellow dust of the Valium was all that remained in the bottle and she could feel bile beginning to rise in her throat as she forced herself now to the bedroom.

Mel lay on top of the bed, her arms around each of her babies. Hannah raced over to the bed; Melanie was still breathing. She put her finger to the neck pulse of each of the children. There was the tiniest fluttering, but only just. Grabbing her mobile phone, Hannah dialled 999, her hands shaking so much she thought she might drop it.

"Emergency! Emergency!" she screamed to the operator, giving the address and shouting that it was a matter of life and death. Now she lifted the younger child, breathing into her mouth, willing her to stay, shouting at Melanie, shaking the other child. Ambulances wailed in the distance, ever nearer as Hannah fought with all the strength she could muster to hold on. "Jesus, Lord God. Help me, help them," she prayed. "Melanie! Melanie!" she shouted. "Hold on! Hold on!"

Later, at the hospital, Hannah pressed her head against the glass window of the children's unit. The two girls lay side-by-side, pink cheeks flushed in their butterfly white cots. Melanie, her head back, was asleep on the chair, her hand through the bars of the nearest cot, clutching the tiny fingers of her youngest child. Her face was relaxed and serene.

Hannah felt a single tear roll down her cheek. In these last short months, she had been faced with the real world. She had witnessed the vagaries of the human spirit, not least her own. She shivered, remembering the look in Estelle's eyes as she slowly turned towards Hannah before the police car drove her away. "My carefree days are gone," she thought. Could she take this responsibility? Was she really cut out for this? She closed her eyes as tiredness overwhelmed her. She knew only one thing: if the young mother before her had the courage to go on, she would be there for her. Their journeys were now inextricably linked. As she turned to leave, she looked through the window one final time to find Melanie awake and smiling up at her.

Days of Wine and Rosaries

"Would you look at that!" The nurse smiled broadly as she peered into the commode. "Good girl, Marnie, a good result," she added, lifting out the pan and deftly covering it with a paper towel. Marnie was bent over, leaning on the handles of the commode, one grey stocking crumpled sadly around her ankle. "Come on, now, that's a girl, fix your skirt" said the nurse, both hands now occupied as she supported Marnie.

"Result?" Marnie warbled, her voice tremulous as froth. "Are the results in?"

"Just fix your skirt, now, Marnie. Come on, reach round and pull it down; you can do it. Good girl," the nurse said, trying to balance with difficulty as Marnie leaned back on her.

"Where's my skirt?" she said, stretching out her hand aimlessly. "Where did I leave it?" she asked, making to sit down again.

"It's on you, Marnie." The exasperation in the young woman's voice was lost on Marnie, who looked up at her, bewildered.

"What's on me?"

"Oh, for goodness sake!" shouted the nurse, the strain of balancing the pan and Marnie becoming too much. "Here, move round a bit," she said, biting her lip in concentration as she stretched out to grab hold of the skirt. Unfortunately, Marnie chose that moment to swing around, causing the girl to overbalance and drop the pan. "Oh, my God!" the nurse cried as the subject of the recent celebration shot sloppily over the polished linoleum floor. Marnie started to laugh, a high-pitched giggle, as the nurse quickly adjusted the clothes and led her back to the sitting room.

"God give me strength," she muttered, her face a rictus of restraint. The only other trained staff nurse hadn't turned in that day; still, only another hour before the night shift would relieve her. It had been a long day. Thank God the numbers were well down, she thought. A few deaths made all the difference. Helping Marnie into her chair, she looked across at the two other residents, whose benevolent expressions summoned an unbidden thought to her mind: "People are living far too long these days. Mind you, these three are in a class of their own; all as mad as March Hares." Still, there was work to be done . . .

"I'll have to get this cleaned up now. I'm on my own today, girls, so no more requests; you'll just have to wait. What is it, Jane?" the nurse exhaled loudly, dragging her hand through her hair. Jane, a white-bunned little lady, sat very straight in her chair, feeding her rosary through her fingers. The beads, which she maintained came from the pope himself, lay over the grey nun's habit of her own designing. Her hand was raised in question.

"I need to get the vestments ready for Mass."

"I told you before, Jane, this isn't the chapel. Now just sit quiet there until I get back."

"Can I have a sherry?" asked Marnie, inclining her head towards the dark walnut sideboard where the sherry bottle and three dainty glasses sat on a silver tray.

"You know you don't get sherry until dinnertime, Marnie," said the nurse. She thought to herself, "I could do with one myself today; roll on the happy hour." Then she looked at her charges and said, "Now, no more questions until I wipe up this bloody mess."

After the job was done, the heavily built nurse, face flushed with exertion, walked briskly through to the adjoining room to check on her other residents.

Marnie waited until she was out of earshot, then whispered to Cassie and Jane, "That big girl must be new. I haven't seen her before." The two ladies stared straight ahead – Jane reciting her prayers with fervid concentration and Cassie humming gently.

After a while, Jane's chanting stopped and she turned to Cassie, pointing up to an image of the Sacred Heart. "Who's that wee critter over there?" she asked. "He's been sitting up there all day, looking over at me and not saying a word."

"Seven o'clock," said Cassie, smiling.

Marnie, meanwhile, was concentrating on her loosened stocking. The marked curvature of her spine made it uncomfortable for her to raise her head, reducing her vista, in the main, to floor level. With painstaking patience, she now pulled at her stocking until it came off. Then, very slowly, she began folding it over and over in perfect little symmetrical shapes until she was left with a small, fat triangle of silk. She drew it gently across her face, glancing at her two companions before concealing it neatly inside her thermal vest.

"The school bell's very late today," she said. "I wonder where my class has gone . . . I need to get them ready for the inspection. Oh, Lord, I nearly forgot about the medical inspection. Is it today?" she leaned over towards Jane.

"Nurse Pitts has fits when she sees nits," lilted Jane, her hooded eyes bloodshot against her dough-white skin.

Cassie raised herself straighter in the chair, her fingers steepled as she nodded. "Nit, the egg of the head louse, *pediculus humanus capitis,*" she said. "Feeds off the blood on the scalp, nasty little creature. I saw a child in my surgery yesterday; the poor mother was distraught because the child was having repeated episodes." Cassie sighed and raised a hand to her temple. The tiniest grace note of a frown began to furrow her distinctive brow. "Who are those children in the corner?" she suddenly asked.

Jane started forward as if listening: "Oh good, good." She clapped her hands.

"Is that my class? Where are they?" lamented Marnie.

"They're over there, jumping up and down," Cassie said.

"I can't see them," Marnie wailed. "They'll be late for the inspection."

Jane was up from her seat now, swaying and singing at the top of her voice.

"What's going on here?" the nurse cried, clapping her hands authoritatively as she strode briskly back to the room.

Marnie was halfway to her feet, her body bent at an angle of forty-five degrees. "Get over here, girls," she warbled. "The inspector's coming."

Jane was reciting the rosary, eyes lifted to heaven as the nurse looked at the scene before her with mounting impatience. "Sit down, Marnie. God of almighty, what's going on?" she cried.

"It's those children in the corner," said Cassie.

"Now, Cassie, I've told you before. There's only you, Marnie and Jane." She enunciated each word in clipped tones. "You're all in a Nursing Home; this is your home now. There are no children in here," she said forcibly.

"Oh, but there are," insisted Cassie. "Over there in the corner."

"Look, Cassie, there's nobody here," said the nurse, moving over to the corner where she began flapping her arms up and down. "It's all in your head."

Cassie sat back, a secret smile on her face.

"Now settle down, the three of you," pleaded the nurse, kneading her fist against her throbbing temple. "My blood pressure must be through the roof," she thought to herself. "Marnie. Where's your stocking?" she demanded. "I've told you a hundred times about keeping your clothes."

"Not telling," Marnie giggled, putting a finger to her lips.

"Marnie!" the warning voice repeated.

Suddenly, Cassie burst out laughing. "Fooled you, fooled you," she shrieked. "They're in the other corner."

Jane now joined in. "Nurse Pitts has nits. Nurse Pitts has nits. Hail Mary full of grace, have you any wool?" she chanted, clapping her hands.

For a brief moment, the nurse thought she would join them; she was losing her reason. Where the hell were the night shift? "Stop it! Stop it!" she shouted out loud. "Marnie, where is your stocking? I know you've hidden it again. Where is it? Give it to me now or no sherry tonight." Suddenly, it all became too much. "Keep quiet, you raving lunatics!" she roared. "Shut up!"

Cassie stopped laughing immediately, the expression on her face lifting as though a blind had been drawn back. "Don't shout, Nurse," said Cassie. "We can hear. Marnie, give the nurse your stocking. you'll get a cold. When you have a moment, Nurse, she could do with a blast of her nebuliser. She was a bit wheezy during the night."

The nurse, who had been caring for Cassie for two years, now recognised one of the elderly doctor's rare pockets of lucidity, and with all the skill and wisdom of her vocation, eased back from the edge of her intolerance. "Sorry, Cassie. I'm under pressure here today. Staff shortage and all. I'll see to it in a minute . . . when I get a chance," she added as Marnie produced the stocking, pulling down her vest and exposed the criss-cross welts of a primitive mastectomy.

"Good girl, Marnie," she said. "Let me fix your blouse," she added gently, never failing to be touched by the old lady's scars. "Thank God for modern medicine," she thought. "The old girl has done well to survive. I'd better be careful with my temper and go easy on them. Though God knows they'd put you astray in the head."

She leaned on the edge of the chair now to lever herself down to her knees and replace Marnie's stocking, just as the dinner bell rang from the kitchen.

"Jesus, Mary and Joseph, it's Mass time," Jane called out, rising from the chair and reaching for her stick.

"What's the time? Is that the time? Oh, my God, he must be here. I have to go, I have to go," said Marnie, all her limbs now moving as though commanded by an invisible puppeteer.

"Stay at peace, Marnie, till I get this on," muttered the nurse between clenched teeth, at the same time reaching over towards Jane. "Jane, sit down, you're going to fall," she cried as Jane teetered precariously above her.

Just at that, Marnie shot forward in her seat, her head clashing against the nurse's bent head. The force of the blow unbalanced the nurse, who fell back awkwardly, her head snapping upwards, just as Jane finally lost her balance and fell heavily on top of her with an ominous crack.

"Goodness gracious!" exclaimed Cassie. "Are you all right?" She leaned over to where Jane lay winded, the bent legs of the nurse splayed beneath her. Marnie sat immobile in her chair, her eyes closed. "Nurse, are you all right?" Cassie called, tentatively at first, then louder. "Nurse, Nurse, can you hear me?" Reaching for her Zimmer frame, Cassie struggled painfully to her feet, shuffling the two or so paces to where Jane lay. Surveying the scene, with the fading practised eye of her late profession, she began to prod Jane with her shoe in an effort to bring her around. Getting no response, she moved slowly over towards Marnie and, reaching down, shook her; gently at first, then with more urgency.

"Marnie, do you hear me? Marnie, open your eyes." She bent over then and placed her hand on Marnie's forehead; an angry bump was emerging from the pallid skin. "Better out than in," she thought. Then, hearing the gentle susurrus of her snoring, Cassie realised that, at worst, Marnie would have a sore head when she woke up.

She stood for a minute, unsure of what to do next. Clouds were beginning to form again; her head felt a little fuzzy. She knew there was something else she should be doing, but for the life of her didn't know what it was.

Cassie shuffled back to where Jane lay, now moaning. "Hold on to this and help yourself up," she told Jane.

"Where am I?' said Jane.

"You fainted, dear," Cassie could hear herself say, although she had no idea what this meant. Her anxiety was rising as she tried to claw back the dissipating threads of her memory.

Fainted. The word seemed alien to her. "Faint, fainted, simple faint," she called out loud as Jane rose to her feet clinging onto the Zimmer frame.

"Faith of our Fathers Holy Faith," sang Jane.

"Faith," echoed Cassie. "Faith, faint, faith…yes that's it," she said uncertainly.

The nurse lay on the ground, her head at a funny angle, a small trickle of blood escaping from her ear. Marnie now stirred in her chair, lamenting, "What time is it? My head hurts," she cried, her voice shaky, a breath away from tears. "Is it time for sherry?"

Jane was still leaning on the Zimmer frame, looking down at the nurse. "Tut, tut," she clucked, her head shaking from side to side. "She's drunk . . . and in the chapel too. She should be horsewhipped."

Cassie looked down at the body on the ground with curiosity. What was it that she should do, she wondered. Marnie was up on her feet, lurching sideways towards the sherry bottle.

"I think . . ." said Cassie. "I think . . ." she said again, but nothing else came as she succumbed to the cocoon of the clouds, a slow smile spreading across her face. "I know," she laughed. "Let's hide."

Jane clapped her hands. "Hide and seek, hide and seek," she sang.

Marnie had no idea how to get the sherry from the bottle to the glass. And so, with a mighty effort, she began swigging the amber liquid as her two friends, attached to their Zimmers, shimmied towards her.

"It's the happy hour,' cheered Cassie, lifting the bottle from Marnie and passing it to Jane, who blessed herself reverentially before downing a mouthful.

Marnie was bent over again, her head bobbing, as though disconnected from her body. "Is it my turn again?" she asked Jane, who hiccoughed before passing the bottle back to Cassie.

"You're next," giggled Cassie, hoisting the bottle to her lips and closing her eyes as the golden liquid coursed like nectar down her throat. "Happy hour," she cheered as the sounds of the nightshift approached in the distance.

"Hide!" squealed Jane. "Hide and seek!"

With Marnie clutching the bottle and clinging precariously to the Zimmer, the trio now shuffled tipsily behind the sideboard and sank bonelessly to the floor in a tangle of arms, legs . . . and rosary beads.

Redemption

Nora gently took her mother's arm, as she stumbled. "Just hold on to me mother. It'll be alright," she said. Maeve smiled at her daughter gratefully before bending again into the chill Atlantic wind. The graveyard in Aranmore was empty as they threaded their way through the grey granite and black marble, stopping now and then as Maeve recognised an old neighbour or friend now gone. Then they were there. Nora let go her mother's arm as Maeve moved forward tentatively to the grave of her beloved parents. "I'm home," she whispered. "I've come home."

Nora was overwhelmed with a kaleidoscope of emotion. "It's over," she thought, "and yet it has only begun." She turned to the dark brooding waters below, as she was transported back to that morning, which seemed like an age ago now, when hope and despair had fused, creating a destiny she had never imagined.

The inchoate morning had struggled towards dawn, seagulls screeched and clamoured above the small fisher boats. The morning ferry was coming into dock, and the islanders, already risen, were busy attending to their daily tasks. Nora Magill had risen early, and drawn a robe around her slender arms, before going downstairs to light the fire. She was eighteen years old and long limbed. A mane of copper-curls, which she hastily pinned back now, framed an intelligent face. The fire lit, Nora called to her grandfather and began making breakfast.

John Magill followed her wearily into the kitchen. His bony frame scaffolded a spotless simmit vest; worn leather braces held up his sagging trousers, and a pale blue shirt, the colour of his eyes, lay tipsily over his arm. Nora smiled as she turned to greet him. "Morning Grandad, how are you feeling this morning?" Before John could answer, he was overwhelmed by a wracking cough, harsh and guttural. As the spasms continued, John held on to the side of the table motioning for a glass of water. When at last the cough subsided, he sat down heavily on the worn leather chair by the fire. Struggling to find his breath he turned to Nora, wiping his brow, "I'm feeling a bit tired today love and I think I'll not bother with breakfast."

Nora busied herself around the kitchen frowning to herself as she felt a vague anxiety steal over her. Her grandfather was all she had in this world. His cough was not going away, and despite medication he was not getting any better. He had been growing more distant recently, staring out at the ocean, wearing a look of unbearable sadness. She worried about him and felt powerless to help him in these days. She moved over now to where he sat, his gnarled hand trembling as he held it over the heat.

"What's the matter Granda, do you not feel well?" she asked, as she hunkered down before him. John looked down at his beloved Granddaughter. "I dreamt of your Grandmother last night Nora, she was dancing and laughing. She wanted me to dance as well and we turned and twirled, spinning wildly across the floor. All our old friends were there, I didn't want to wake up." John sighed deeply as he turned his head towards the door.

"Nora," he said softly as to himself. "Nora, Nora…"

"What is it Granda?" Nora reached over and took his hands in hers, stroking them gently, acutely aware of how cold they were. "Tell me what's the matter."

Her grandfather sighed and with dimmed rheumy eyes pointed to the cupboard above the range. "Do you see the black box up there Nora? Bring it down to me." Nora reached up to the top of the press, puzzled by the despair in his voice. "Is this it Granda?" she asked, stumbling a little as her foot caught on the side of the fender. John lifted the box, all the while his hand trembling, and held it. Then withdrawing a key from his trouser pocket he turned it in the lock.

"I should have told you this a long time ago Nora. Your mother, my daughter, Maeve was as beautiful as you are now but twice as wild, she hated the island and was mad to get onto the mainland at every opportunity. She loved dancing, loved the wildness of the town boys, always complaining of the ruddy-faced boys here. She was like a wild colt, desperate to escape." John stopped, as his eyes glazed over, remembering his beloved only daughter as if it were yesterday.

"Maeve yearned to get away from here, so much so, that she took off one morning and caught the ferry to Burtonport, from there she travelled to Dublin before crossing the sea to England. She sent us cards to the post house so that we would know she was all right, but we never saw her again." John paused as his eyes filled up.

Nora sat in silence but inside she was screaming, "My mother died when I was born!"

Wiping his eyes with the back of his hand John continued:

"It was two years later, when the postmaster's wife, Mrs Bann, arrived at the door to tell us that Maeve had written asking to meet with her in Burtonport. We were confused, why hadn't she asked us, or why didn't she just arrive home. Your grandmother, however, was so excited she immediately began preparations for her homecoming. When Mrs Bann came back with you, wrapped tightly in a warm blanket, we were overwhelmed. It was only then, that I realised Maeve wasn't there. Mrs Bann told us that your mother had a taxi waiting and had been too upset to talk, other than to say that she loved us and she knew we would take care of you. You came only with your birth certificate and a little case of baby clothes. I know now, how Maeve let stupid pride, like mine, stop her from coming home."

Nora shook her head in disbelief. "But Granda, you told me that my mother had died when I was born." John bowed his head.

"Maeve broke your grandmother's heart Nora. She died when you were only two years old. I know she never got over losing her only child, and while you were a blessing, the grief was just too much for her. Years went by and I heard nothing from Maeve, then this letter arrived when you were ten years old. I couldn't give it to you. I was so angry with her, Nora, so angry…"

John's voice broke off thick with emotion. And then with a trembling hand he reached into the box and withdrew a letter, a photograph, and a simple solid silver cross, which he handed to Nora:

My little Nora, this is a hard letter to write. You are ten years old already. I left you when you were only six months old because I was in a very bad place then, and have been for a long time. You needed love and stability and I knew you'd be safe and happy with your grandparents so I took you back home from England. I had hurt my father and mother so much that I couldn't face them and asked Mrs Bann to take you home instead. I was such a coward, but I knew that you would be happy in Aranmore until I could get on my feet. It's been a long journey Nora, I was so unhappy in England but too proud to write and ask to come home. I've been in America now for two years Nora and finally have a job and am feeling good for the first time in years. I miss you so much. I 'm coming home in the autumn, I've nearly saved the fare. I want to see you, see my mother and father, tell them I'm sorry and thank them, O Nora I can't wait to see you. I'm sending you a silver cross I got at the mission out here, I want you to wear it until I see you again, all my love, your mother Maeve.

Nora took her grandfathers hands, as the old man's eyes filled with tears and flowed unchecked down his cheeks:

"I wrote back to Maeve, Nora, I told her that her mother was dead, had died because *she* had broke her heart, told her I didn't want to see her. She didn't come in the autumn, she sent two more letters and I sent them back unopened. Later as you grew up so like your mother, I realised how wrong I was and wrote to Maeve asking her to come home telling her I was sorry. The letter returned, marked 'not at this address'. Nora I'm so sorry. Nothing I can say or do will ever make up for what I did, I've been a bitter old man." John lifted the photograph, his face etched with grief. "This is your mother, taken not long before she left," he said smoothing out the image as though he could touch her face. "You are so like her Nora."

Nora stared at the young woman in the picture. Maeve had turned to the camera just as someone called her, a look of surprise widening her extraordinary green eyes; her hair was haloed by golden sunlight, one blending seamlessly with the other. She was wearing a simple white sleeveless dress, her right shoulder raised flirtatiously to her chin, as she dangled her straw bonnet by her side. As she gazed for the first time on the mother she had never known, Nora was overcome by the likeness. The girl in the picture could have been her. This was her mother. Her thoughts were interrupted as she now focused on her grandfather.

John was agitated and restless, fumbling with the cross and chain. "I want you to wear this cross Nora, put it on, it's your connection to Maeve, it will bring you to her, wear it for me love." Nora's mind was in turmoil as she placed the chain around her neck. Her grandfather was now pacing back and forward, running his hand through his hair over and over. "Shush, Granda, don't worry, its alright, come on, lie down now and I'll bring you a cup of tea Look, I'm wearing the cross, you have a rest and we'll work out what to do later."

Calmness seemed to settle over John then, as he allowed Nora to lead him to the old moquette sofa in the corner, where he soon lapsed into a restless sleep. Nora went back to the fire, stoking the embers before putting more turf on the top. The acrid but fragrant aroma permeated the room and Nora was suddenly filled with a frisson of fear and foreboding. Her mother was alive, all these years. She shivered involuntarily, why was he telling her this now?

Her thoughts were suddenly broken by the onset of an alarming sound from John. A deep and rasping noise as though he was drowning spurred Nora quickly to his side.

"Do you want a drink of water Granda?" she asked alarmed by his pallor and the blue tinges around his lips. John was unable to speak as his gasps became more laboured and collided with the spasms shuddering through his body. He was holding onto Nora now, panic beginning to rise. "I'll get the Doctor, Granda. I'll not be long," Nora leapt to her feet, running to the door and onto the narrow road. "Rose, Rose!" she shouted to her neighbour. "Get the Doctor, get the priest, something's wrong with my grandfather."

She raced back to the house and to her grandfather. John was quite still. Nora knew that he had gone. She sank to her knees shocked to the core. Had he *known* she wondered? She stayed by his side long after the Doctor, the priest and the 'waking' neighbours had gone. She knew what she had to do. Bending close beside his head Nora kissed his brow and whispered to him: "I'll find her, Granda. I'll find her and bring her home."

When the plane came into land, Nora realised she was unconsciously pulling at the silver cross on her neck. Her grandfather's words echoed in her mind – "This is your connection to Maeve, it will bring you to her." As she disembarked at Kennedy Airport Nora held the letter bearing the only address she had for her mother in tight trembling hands. She prayed quietly to her grandfather to guide her now as she ventured forward, her resolve and purpose undiminished by the massive task she faced.

"What's the address again lady?" the taxi man asked as he eyed her through his rear mirror. "Block 64, West 55th street, Queens." Nora sat forward in her seat. "Is it far?" she asked. The taxi man shrugged,

"Be there in about twenty." The front of the building was run down, broken windows jutted through like bits of broken bone. The street was deserted as Nora stepped down from the taxi.

"Would you mind waiting?" she asked the driver nervously. "I don't know if the person I'm looking for still lives here."

"Sure thing lady, don't look much like it's a good neighbourhood, I'll wait right here, go on and knock the door."

Nora gave him a grateful smile as she mounted the few steps to the front door and knocked. When no one answered she knocked again, this time she could hear footsteps slowly approaching on the other side of the door. Nora could hear her heart pounding in her chest as the door opened a fraction. "What do you want?" a sullen voice asked. The woman's face was lined like worn leather. Her hair was greasy and lank and she held a cigarette in her hand.

"I ... I'm looking for my mother," Nora stammered. "Her name is Maeve Magill, she wrote to me from here many years ago."

"Well she's not here now, I've never heard of her, so go away" and she turned to close the door.

"Please, is there anyone else here, anyone who might have known her, anyone else?" Nora's voice trembled, feeling the only link she had, was fading.

"There's no one else here, I'm the only one left in this stinking hell-hole, your mother's one lucky lady, getting out of here," the woman cried before shutting the door firmly in Nora's face.

Nora stood, her head bowed as unbidden tears pricked her eyes.

"Are you alright?" the kindly taxi-man asked. "Come on. I'll take you wherever you need to go next."

"I've got no place to go," Nora's voice broke. "I don't know where to go next."

"Come on then I'll take you over to Hallam's place, you're Catholic right?" he asked.

Nora nodded puzzled as he laughed. "It's the cross, lady, the cross."

Within minutes the taxi driver drew up at Father Hallam's shelter. "You'll be safe here," he said. "Big Father Joe Hallam will sort you out." Nora thanked the man for his kindness and walked up to the Shelter. She was quickly shown in to Father Hallam's office. Snow had fallen earlier and the bitter evening now contrasted dramatically with the warm fire burning in the grate. Father Hallam was a great bear of a man; his face was pockmarked and a long jagged scar stretched from cheekbone to chin. His presence would have been intimidating were it not for the disarming lop-sided grin, which he wore now as he came forward to meet Nora. He strode into the room, dwarfing the place with his presence.

"Hi there," he said. "Who have we here then?"
The lost trail for her mother, the loss of her beloved Grandfather, and the strong friendly handshake of the priest finally became too much for Nora, and she broke down sobbing as though her heart would break.

"There, there child, come on, sit down here, I'll get you a cup of good strong tea." Over the next hour Nora told Fr. Hallam her story between sips of tea and silent tears. When she had finished the priest stood up and walked to his desk. "You'll stay here then Nora," he said. "This is a big community, but it's still a community and we have many links. You tell me that your mother wrote saying she got your cross at a mission. That's where we'll start. There aren't too many in the parish she left. I'll make some calls. You go now and get a rest, you can stay in my housekeeper's room, she's gone home for the week."

Nora thanked him gratefully as he led her to the small room at the top of the hall. She had no sooner laid her head down than she fell into the most restful sleep she'd known since her grandfather died. Over the next few days, Nora helped out in the Shelter as Fr Hallam called on his contacts for news of Maeve. By the end of the week Nora was beginning to despair of finding her mother when the priest unexpectedly called her down to his office. His face was grave and for a moment Nora thought that her mother might be dead.

"There's no easy way to say this Nora, I think I know where your mother is, but, if this is your mother, she's in pretty bad shape. An old colleague of mine Fr Dan Canning rang this morning. He had seen the bulletin I circulated in the parishes and thought he might know your mother's whereabouts, but I must warn you, what he told me was pretty grim. The Maeve he knew did some volunteer work for him many years ago. She was well-liked and was a good worker. She left abruptly one summer telling Fr Canning she had received bad news from home. He discovered later that her mother had died. Maeve fell in with bad company and began drinking, she never returned to her work.

It was Christmas Eve a year ago when he last saw her .She had many bruises, he said, which she tried to cover up. The man she stays with is a local publican with a bad reputation; he had beaten her up pretty bad. Dan tried to persuade her to leave him, but his sense was that her spirit was broken. The key to all this Nora is that shortly before she left her job, Maeve bought a silver cross at one of the mission sales. She told Fr Canning she had bought it to send to her daughter, the daughter she had left behind in Ireland." Fr Hallam paused, "Your journey may be over Nora."

Nora spoke quietly, almost to herself: "My Grandfather told me that this cross would bring me to my mother. Did you get an address Father?" she asked, aware that she was trembling violently. Father Hallam left the room returning with the address a few moments later. "I'll come with you," he said.

As they stood before the door of the public house Nora looked up. The publican's name, J.P. Sheerin, was written across the frontispiece. The letter P had dislodged and lay at an angle, swinging slowly in the breeze. Nora shuddered involuntarily, and then braced herself. This was her reason for coming here, her destiny, nothing would stop her bringing her mother home. Fr Hallam squeezed her arm reassuringly.

The two entered the dimly lit bar. Tobacco smoke hung in stale grey hammocky swathes. Four or five customers sat at the bar. An old woman, merging with the shadows in the corner, wore layers of black wool shawls, her hair yellowed by the smoke. She gently cradled her porter glass, as her cat stretched and yawned on her lap.

"Can I help you?" a gruff and unfriendly voice sliced through the gloom. "I'm looking for Maeve Magill," Nora's voice trembled but she fought back the urge to cry. "Who's asking?" the voice continued. "This is her daughter," the priest said as he strode purposefully into the centre of the bar. The occupants now looked at the strangers, a moment of interest in their drab worlds.

"Her daughter?" the hoarse voice croaked mockingly. "That old hag, you must be joking, what man would lie with her, she has no daughter, there's more life in Moll's old cat over there, isn't that right Molly?"

"You're right Mr Sheerin, give us another half would ye?" the old woman replied.

"I want to see my mother now," Nora moved into the light, as the barman drew the pump handle down, sloshing the porter into a grimy glass. He looked at her with disdain, his steel grey eyes cold and hard. "Take a good look missy," he pointed to a shape in the corner behind him. "That's your mother then, or the cat's mother," he cackled.

Nora moved tentatively forward. Maeve was bent over, half leaning against the kegs of beer in the corner. Nora could only see one half of her face but she knew in her soul this was her mother. "Hey you!" Sheerin suddenly shouted. "Get up, there's somebody here to see you."

As the silence seemed to lengthen into forever, the figure in the corner rose and came towards the front of the bar. Nora held her breath as her mother came into sight. Despite the dark rings beneath her eyes and the ugly yellowing bruise on her temple, it was clear that the woman who stood before her had once been very beautiful. Her dark red hair had lost its lustre and grey streaks fanned her temples. Fire had been replaced by defeat, in her now vacant stare, and her full lips were white, almost merging with the deathly pallor of her skin.

Nora moved closer, "Mother, it's me, it's your daughter Nora." Maeve Magill now lifted her head slowly, her expression blank and uncomprehending.

"Mother, it is me. I've come to bring you home."

"Home," the woman echoed. "Home, what's that? I've got no home. Here, this is my home." She turned to go back to her chair, as the barman laughed out loud. "See, what did I tell you, soft in the head, stupid cow."

"Stop that!" Nora raised her voice to the man before her. "How dare you talk about my mother like that, how dare you treat her like that, my God, what have you done to her?" Her voice tailed off as a welter of emotion took over.

Fr Hallam moved forward. "Maeve," he said quietly. "Maeve, this is your child, Nora. Don't you remember? You told Fr Canning about her, try to remember," he added gently. Maeve continued to stare blankly at the people before her. "My God, Sheerin what have you done? I'll see you in gaol for this, you've beaten her once too often" the priest said, as he turned to face the barman.

"What's it to you, she's nobody, just a waste of space, take your preaching face elsewhere, she's going nowhere, not now, not ever,"

Sheerin suddenly hissed, and moved out from behind the bar snarling dangerously. "I'm taking her now," the priest said. "Come on Maeve, you're leaving him. I'm going to take you to the Shelter."

"Get away from her, get the hell out! She's going nowhere with you, didn't you hear what I said?" Sheerin's eyes looked almost feral in the gloom. Suddenly he reached behind the bar and drew a handgun. "Get the hell out of my place now, or I won't be responsible for what happens!" he said with deadly menace.

Nora stood rooted to the spot. She felt as though she was a player in some grotesque drama. Her eyes never left her mother. She was aware of the priest moving slowly towards the publican. "Give me that Sheerin, don't be stupid, come on, give it up." The other customers now backed away, wary and frightened in the mounting tension. "Give it to me man, this is dangerous," Fr Hallam said, still closing in on the barman.

A faltering voice suddenly spoke from the darkness. "Nora?" Maeve said, hesitatingly at first. "Nora?" she said a second time. Sheerin swung around as Maeve stood, her eyes fastened on the young woman. "Nora, can this really be you? My child, my little girl," she reached forward tentatively.

Seizing the advantage, Fr Hallam sprang forward, grasped Sheerin's arm and was grappling to disarm him, when all of a sudden, a yellow burst of flame ripped through the darkness as the gun discharged its deadly fire. Nora sank to the ground in slow motion. The occupants at the bar scattered in clumsy chaos, as a long-sustained wail, like the cry of lost souls, came from Maeve.

Fr Hallam's huge body had pinned Sheerin to the ground, as he shouted to the huddled group on the floor: "Get 911 now. Hurry, get up, do it!" he commanded, then dragging Sheerin across the room he turned to one of the men, handing him the gun, "Don't let him out of your sight."

Maeve was holding her daughter's head, her eyes wide with shock and disbelief. "Nora, Nora. Help her, please God, help her!' cried Maeve imploring Fr Hallam who now stood above them. The priest bent down, reaching across Maeve to feel for a pulse. A long sigh rose from him as he closed his eyes. Placing his hand on her temple he drew back the hair to reveal a long graze where the bullet had scorched her skin. "It missed her Maeve, it missed. Look, feel her neck," and he took Maeve's hand, guiding it to her daughter's pulse which was strong and steady.

Nora stirred then in her mother's arms, opening her eyes, confused at first as she looked at the anxious faces above her, then suddenly smiling. "I had a sense of my Granda just now, pulling me towards him, it must have been just before I fell," she looked at her mother. "His arms were so strong." Nora looked around as though she expected her Grandfather to be there. "It seemed so real," she said. Her voice was quiet now, her eyes filling with tears, "I miss him so much, Mother. Can we go home?"

Maeve shivered, as she bent forward and kissed Nora's brow. "I miss him too," she whispered. "Take me home Nora, take me home."

AUTHOR BIOGRAPHICAL DETAILS

DR ARTHUR MITCHELL has lived and worked as a family doctor in the Mourne area for over forty years. Now retired, he retains a deep interest in the welfare of its rural communities and in conservation. He is actively involved with others in promoting the concept and creation of a Celtic National Park in the Mournes.

BERNADETTE BECKETT was born in Belfast and now lives in Hillsborough with her husband and three small sons. She works part-time in education and says that she used to have lots of hobbies and interests which she hopes to return to, some day.

PAT HEANEY is a former Special Needs teacher and the mother of three "apparently grown-up" children. Since returning to Derry six years ago, after spending much of her adult life in London, she has enjoyed writing short stories. Several of these have been published in local, community anthologies. Her other interests include music and socialising, and immersing herself in the rugged landscape of nearby Donegal.

BRIDIE TIMMONS is a former Vice-Principal of St Anne's School in Strabane. She is a theatre enthusiast, who also enjoys writing and producing short plays. She believes that life itself provides her with all the inspiration she needs for her writing.

TOMMY THOMPSON lives in Belfast and is a former engineer with the Civil Aviation Authority. He is a partner in the family-owned chain of Bargain Bookshops. His interests include aviation, museum projects, band music and playing the accordion, as well as history and community activities

MICHELLE McEVOY lives near Banbridge, and works as a PA. She has been writing poetry and prose in her spare time since 2004, and recently spent some time in Australia.

ANNE-MARIE FITZPATRICK lives in Belfast and is a frequent visitor to Dunfanaghy. She first began to write during the weekend workshops in Arnold's Hotel, and treasures her meeting with a former American President.

DAVID TIERNEY is a businessman who is also a consultant in Lifestyle and Stress-management. He first worked with Alf McCreary on writing sessions in conjunction with the Institute of Lifelong Learning at Queen's University. This is his first collection of stories.

STELLA MITCHELL spent some 30 years in Social Work. Following her retirement, she retains her interest in Mental Health by working as an independent social worker, with a special regard for "Women's Issues." She enjoys reading and the Classical Theatre, and attends the Royal Shakespeare Company's productions at Stratford-upon-Avon, where her son is the leading actor, Will Houston. Her lifelong interest in writing has blossomed again in her "retirement".

PHILIP GORMLEY comes from the townland of Carnanbane, Claudy, and now lives in Magherafelt, where he had been in practice as a Chartered Accountant until his retirement for health reasons. He has always sought to know his native land in all its practical aspects, and not least in its intriguing history and complex geology.

FIONNUALA McGOWAN was born in Derry and studied English Literature in Dublin before embarking on a vocational journey in Social Work. She is the proud mother of five "almost-reared" children, who have inherited her deep love of literature and music, and who ply their creative talents far and wide.